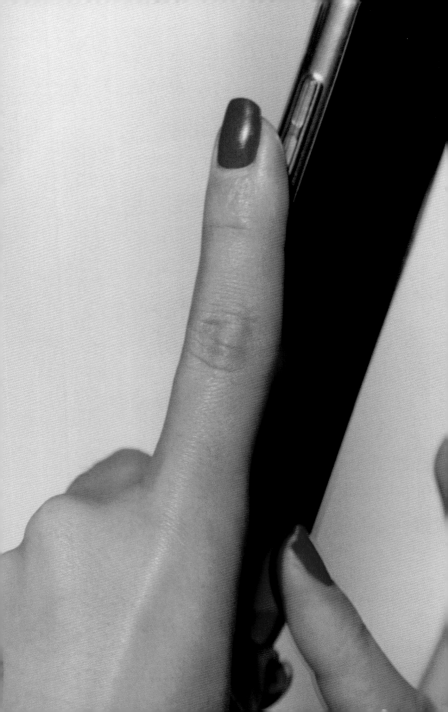

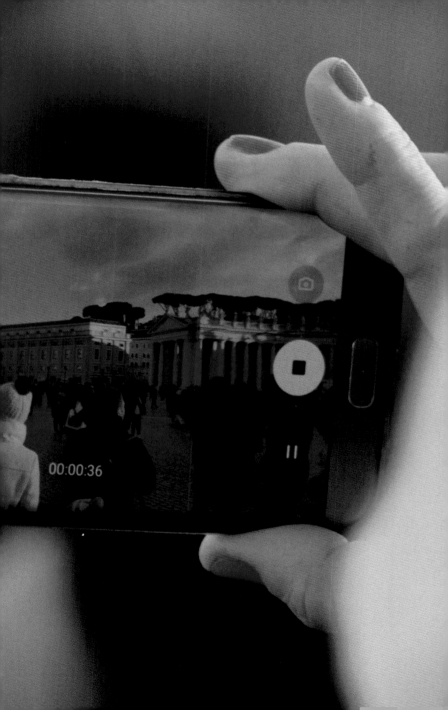

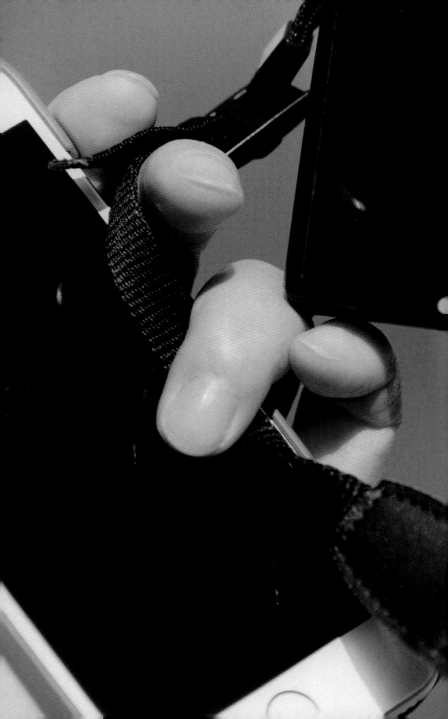

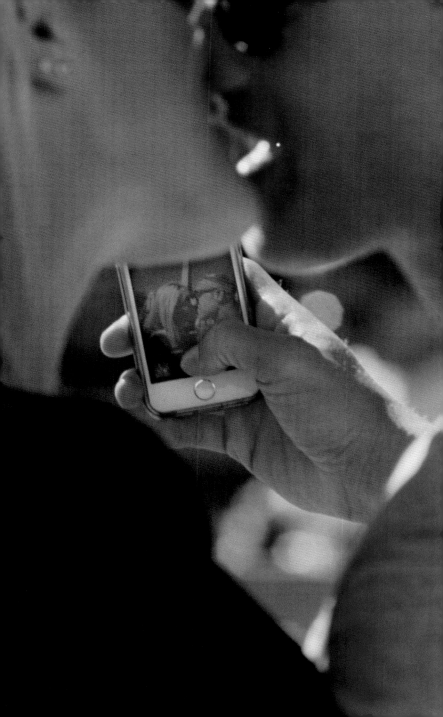

Thomas Adank   Photographer, London. He studied at ECAL and at the Royal College of Art. He lectures at Camberwell College of Arts.

Andrea Bagnato   Architect and researcher, Milan. He started the project *Terra Infecta* in 2013 to study the spatial and ecological history of infectious diseases. He was head of publications for the first Sharjah Architecture Triennial and teaches at Willem de Kooning Academy.

Shumon Basar   Writer, editor and curator, London. He is co-author of *The Extreme Self* (2021), commissioner of the Global Art Forum and a member of the Fondazione Prada Thought Council.

Crystal Bennes   Artist, writer, curator and researcher, Edinburgh. She curated exhibitions at the Venice Architecture Biennale and for her own curatorial project *SALON* in London. She is a PhD candidate at the BxNU Institute and Cultural Negotiation of Science research group, at Northumbria University.

Disnovation   Art collective founded by Nicolas Maigret and Maria Roszkowska. It is engaged in the crossovers between contemporary art, research and hacking. Their project *Shanzhai Archaeology* (2015–2018), with collaborators Clément Renaud and Yuan Qu, was exhibited in London and Nantes.

Paul Elliman   Artist, London. He was included in the Liverpool Biennial in 2018, and teaches a class at the Yale School of Art called Quale Song, exploring the social histories of song. He has exhibited at the ICA, MoMA and Tate Modern.

Gabriella Garcia   Writer, performer and poetic technologist, New York. She is a postdoctoral fellow at New York University's (NYU) Interactive Telecommunication Program and acting managing editor of *Adjacent*, NYU's journal for emergent interactive media. She sits on the Community Advisory Board for the Urban Justice Center's Surveillance Technology Oversight Project (STOP).

Orit Gat   Writer on contemporary art and digital culture, London. She is currently working on her first book, *If Anything Happens*, about football.

Elisa Giuliano   Architect, researcher and choreographer, Milan. She was head of exhibition design for the Fondazione Matera 2019 and a fellow at Ocean Space/ TBA21 in 2020. She is currently completing an MFA at the Dutch Art Institute.

Ajay Hothi   Writer on art, design, film and sport, London. He is a senior lecturer in Critical Studies at Kingston and London Metropolitan universities. He writes for *Artforum*, *Art in America* and *Frieze*.

Rhianna Jones   Writer, advocate and model, New York. Her work champions cultural inclusivity, sustainability and Afrocentric beauty norms and has been featured in *The New York Times*, *NowThis News* and in the anthology *Black Futures* (2020).

CONTRIBUTORS

Anniina Koivu Design writer, curator and consultant, Milan and Lausanne, and Head of Master Theory at ECAL.

Lucie Krahulcova Professional activist, policy analyst and digital rights advocate, Melbourne. She is executive director of Digital Rights Watch in Australia.

Joe Lloyd Writer on architecture, art and design, London. He has written for a range of publications on forensics, design patents, restoration, EpiPens and the dying of prawns.

Joanne McNeil Technology writer, New England. She is author of *Lurking* (2020) and winner of a Carl & Marilynn Thoma Art Foundation's Arts Writing Award. She was resident at Eyebeam, a Logan Nonfiction Program fellow and an instructor at the School for Poetic Computation.

Francesco Nazardo Artist, London. His photography has featured in *T Magazine*, *Buffalo Zine* and *Vogue Italia*.

Lizzie O'Shea Lawyer, writer and advocate for human rights online, Melbourne. She is the founder of Digital Rights Watch in Australia. Her book *Future Histories* (2019), applies theory to debates about digital technology.

Jay Owens Researcher and media and technology writer, London. Her work has featured on *BBC Radio 4*, *The Guardian*, in design publications and in the anthology *Post-Memes: Seizing the Memes of Production* (2019).

Bryony Quinn Writer, editor and lecturer, London. She is co-editor of design research journal *Bricks from the Kiln #4*. Her writing has been published by Reaktion Books and *Failed States*. She teaches at the Royal College of Art.

Tobias Revell Digital artist and designer, London. He is a PhD candidate at Goldsmiths University and programme director at the London College of Communication. He co-founded design research consultancy Strange Telemetry, critical technology outfit Supra Systems Studios and research and curatorial project *Haunted Machines*.

Stéphanie Saadé Artist, Beirut, Paris and Amsterdam. She was artist in residence at Jan van Eyck Academie. Her work was shown at the 13th Sharjah Biennial, Punta Della Dogana (Venice) and MOCA (Toronto) and she has had various solo exhibitions.

Nicole Starosielski Associate Professor of Media, Culture and Communication, New York University. She is author of *The Undersea Network* (2015) and *Media Hot and Cold* (2021).

Chen Weihan Independent curator, Taiwan. She holds an MA in Curating Contemporary Design from Kingston University. She is event planner of *Nuit Blanche* Taipei (2021).

Liam Young Speculative architect and film director, LA. He is co-founder of urban futures think tank Tomorrows Thoughts Today and nomadic research studio Unknown Fields.

DIRTY FURNITURE   #5 PHONE

Published in London,
September 2021

Editors
Anna Bates, Elizabeth Glickfeld

Sub-editors
Mike Gautrey, George Kafka

Editorial assistants
Rosalita Baldassin, Lara Machado

Design and art direction
Studio Mathias Clottu

Printing
Printon AS, Estonia

*Advertising, sponsorship
and distribution*
info@dirty-furniture.com

Thank you Lara Chapman,
Gabriella Garcia, Charmian Griffin,
Suzanne Kite, Frankie Moutafis,
Francesca Sobande, Steve Watson

Subscribe
Buy issues online at
www.dirty-furniture.com

Submissions
Please email the editors if you have
a proposal for our next issue – Bed
– and tell us a bit about yourself.

Contact
editors@dirty-furniture.com

Distribution
UK Central Books
magazines@centralbooks.com

Europe, USA and Australasia
Idea Books idea@ideabooks.nl

Rest of world Please contact us
directly at info@dirty-furniture.com

Cover image
front Kim Kardashian West tweets
a photo of herself being made-up
to promote her brand KKW
Beauty, December 23, 2019.
back Electromagnetic simulation
of a 28-GHz series-fed patch antenna
array for 5G; Visitors take pictures
of tidal waves under the influence
of Typhoon Usagi in Hangzhou,
September 2013.

Images throughout
Francesco Nazardo, 2018–2021,
from his book *Francesco Nazardo
Photos*, £30.

ISBN 978-0-9933511-3-6
ISSN 2055-7051

At the beginning of 2020, when we began commissioning this issue of *Dirty Furniture*, the ether was rife with negativity about the way we use our phones. *The Guardian* reported that nearly a quarter of young people have a problematic relationship with their phone. Books addressing phone addiction became bestsellers. We were encouraged to be mindful of our screen time and to cultivate 'digital wellness'.

Then the pandemic hit. Suddenly these maligned objects became our lifelines. While many aspects of life passed through our phones previously, now absolutely everything did. How then could we distil the meaning of the phone into a magazine?

We used the moment to pivot: to question and reassess. In April 2020, as London went into lockdown, we ran *Dirty Furniture Calling...* a series of live phone calls with design's great minds talking about love, work, distraction, life – and of course, phones – in the somewhat alienating time of social distancing.

We have emerged from the onset of the pandemic the same but different. Our new *Dirty Furniture*, conceived over the phone and designed by Studio Mathias Clottu, combines the joy of a glossy with the practicality of a book. Inside, we propose multiple ways of thinking about this digital prosthesis – how we use it, and how it uses us. Let us know what you think – we'll be checking our phones.

Anna Bates and Elizabeth Glickfeld

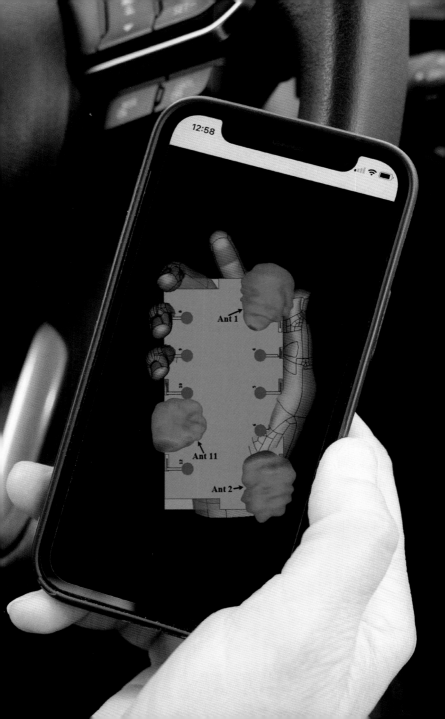

WHEN HE DIED IN 2007
FROM A HEART ATTACK,
HE WAS COMMEMORATED
WITH A FOUR-HOUR
CONFERENCE CALL

€45,000 and a year in jail by Lucie Krahulcova,
Why did you leave the house with your phone? by
Lara Machado, Just setting up my twttr by Orit Gat,
The phreaker by Joe Lloyd, Independent dialling by
Anniina Koivu, Koumpounophobia by Bryony Quinn,
The history of necromancy by Tobias Revell.

A telephone operator in the 1930s

€45,000 and a year in jail
Paris, France

In November 2020, President Macron announced a new plan as a part of his global security law: to criminalise both the filming of police officers as they carry out their duties and the sharing of such content online.

The proposed law continues the government's ruthless approach to national security since the 2015 terror attacks. France has had one of the longest state-of-emergency orders (where government holds extraordinary powers to interrogate citizens and conduct searches and arrests) in all of Europe. So its intentions shouldn't come as a surprise.

Smartphones allow us to document almost any event at the touch of a fingertip. During the Arab Spring, or more recently the Hong Kong protests, as international newsrooms faced political and practical pressure from authorities, footage from citizens coloured and defined the international narrative. Where we would previously get hearsay, we got eyewitness evidence; we saw the size of the crowds and understood the scale of the seismic events that were taking place. But this new tool has not sat well with everyone: law enforcement and governments have not welcomed the smartphone's capacity to document events.

Around the world, footage from smartphones has become a point of controversy for national authorities. During protests or political unrest, authoritarian governments have shut down the entire country's internet to prevent communities organising on social media and sharing footage with international news outlets. Earlier this year, the Iranian government cut off internet access in two provinces to hide human rights violations. In March, India used the same tactic to keep footage of farmers' protests offline. While this strategy may violate human rights, it is not an overreaction – the internet has proved itself to be powerful. The viral potential of videos frightens those who want to hold onto power. Authoritarian governments aren't alone in their fear, as Macron's announcement

FIRST INSTAGRAM POST

A dog
by Kevin Systrom, 2010

demonstrates. The conversations which have been sparked by citizen footage of police brutality and racial injustice in liberal democracies undermine the international standing of those governments.

Article 24 of the proposed French law does not completely ban sharing images of the police, but makes it a crime to do so with the 'obvious intent to cause harm' to police officers. This of course is an interesting legal concept to ponder, because there is a difference between intent and unintended consequences. When sharing a video of police violence or abuse of power at a protest, for instance, most of us would have the intent to bring justice to the victims and the situation. Harm to the reputation of the police officer may be a consequence of that. However, should someone who perpetrates injustice be immune from harm because they are a police officer? In a constitutional democracy such as France, shouldn't the pursuit of justice always override any potential harm to the state?

France's highest authority on the constitution would seem to agree. It rejected the article earlier this year.

The Constitutional Council ruled that the legislature did not sufficiently define the elements which would constitute the offence in such cases. Much like us, they wondered what intent to cause harm would look like, how it would be proved or even what constitutes a police operation. While this may seem like a victory, the Court essentially sent the article back on a technicality, and asked the government to clearly define what it meant.

For now, the power given to citizens by smartphones will continue to terrify those it threatens. But it will require a global alliance of all of us to make sure we retain that power, because the future of the smartphone as a witness depends on a collective determination to defend it.

Lucie Krahulcova

Roadside cameras catch drivers using their phones

Why did you leave the house with your phone? Fortaleza, Brazil

Two women attending a party are held hostage by armed thieves for 20 minutes. Their phones are stolen, but only one of the women loses her working phone. The other was carrying a 'bandit's phone'.

Carrying a bandit's phone – an old or broken device – is common practice in Fortaleza. The capital of Ceará State and one of Brazil's

Jacques Tati in his film *Jour de Fête* (1949)

biggest cities, Fortaleza is constantly featured in the top 10 most dangerous cities in the world. According to the Superintendency of Public Security Research and Strategy, 43,943 thefts were reported in the state in 2020. Many more were not even reported. Losing your phone has become so common that the victim rather than the thief is blamed: 'Why didn't you have your extra phone with you? Why did you leave the house with your personal phone? Why did you use your phone outdoors?' We tend to forget it is the system that should be blamed.

The high levels of urban violence in Fortaleza are a product of unprecedented structural inequality. Many reasons have been given: racism, a punitive prison system, little investment in education, economic crisis, unemployment, lack of access and opportunity. Some even profit from urban violence, like the security and insurance industries. The prevalence of the extra bandit phone goes some way to explaining why the 425 million phones in Brazil come to almost double its population. Human dependency on these devices is dangerous in Fortaleza. Lives are lost on both sides: either by hesitating to relinquish a phone or by having to steal one to survive.   *Lara Machado*

Just setting up my twttr
California, USA

Is a tweet comparable to the *Mona Lisa*? Tech entrepreneur and cryptocurrency investor Sina Estavi thought it was when in March 2021, three months after its listing on digital auction platform Valuables, he bought the first tweet for $2.9 million. The tweet, by Twitter co-founder Jack Dorsey, reads 'just setting up my twttr'.

Valuables is dedicated to selling tweets as non-fungible tokens, or NFTs. Many people learned what NFTs are in the last few years, when sums of millions of dollars started being traded for them. Essentially, NFTs allow editioning of digital objects. When a digital photo, a tweet or a meme is sold as an NFT, it is minted on a blockchain with a certificate of authenticity that proves ownership. A token is thus not dissimilar to a cryptocurrency, just that in this case it is a unique object.

But how unique is a tweet, a meme, a video, a sound? The language around NFTs – words such as 'unique' and 'authentic' – contradicts the duplicable nature of digital media. The Disaster Girl meme (the little girl looking cheekily, self-satisfied, at the camera in front of a burning house) sold as an NFT for $473,000. The photograph was taken by amateur photographer Dave Roth, of his daughter Zoë, when they went to see a controlled burn. It won a photography award, after which it went viral. Disaster Girl is not famous because it won an award, or for its artistic merit,

but for how the image shifted in meaning once it went viral and was exploited by internet users posting it time and again in different contexts. How do we qualify the value, or worth, of a meme or a tweet? The answer is in its distribution.

When Estavi purchased Dorsey's tweet, he argued on Twitter that it's not 'just a tweet' and that 'years later people will realize the true value of this tweet, like the Mona Lisa painting'. Estavi's argument that people will come to see the value of this tweet means he sees it for what it is: a token. Value is another example of a word that, in this context, combines both material and immaterial significance. Is a tweet worth $2.9 million? Anything is worth as much as someone is willing to pay for it. (Estavi beat millionaire entrepreneur Justin Sun, who also made his fortune off cryptocurrency, in the auction, with Sun offering $2.5 million.) Its value is financial, a log of what someone was willing to pay for it. And it has a historical, symbolic value, which is what Estavi is arguing for with his *Mona Lisa* comparison.

And so, what actually sold is not the tweet – the tweet is still online, available for anyone to see, respond to or repost – but the tweet's symbolic value, as a marker of a significant moment in digital cultural history. There is a bot on Twitter called @VeryOldTweets, which retweets one of the first 7,500 tweets from the first 90 days of Twitter in 2006. It cycles through them four times a day, randomly. 'Old tweets are kind of weird,' the account's bio reads, and it's true. 'Ironing a shirt' and 'having some

FIRST MEME

Cats: All Your Base are Belong to Us
A mistranslation from Japanese
arcade game *Zero Wing*, 1998

Michael Douglas in the film *Wall Street* (1987)

coffee', early tweets by Biz Stone, another Twitter co-founder, seem like chewed-up examples of how useless 'microblogging', as tweets were initially explained, may be. These bear no relation to the professionalised, news-oriented platform that Twitter became.

In my 2021 Twitter timeline, the 2006 tweets feel ghostly, like a past signalling a future that never happened. That said, I am happy users don't really post 'just getting coffee', instead opting for news and jokes, opinions and real connections – evidence of a life lived online. 'Just setting up my twttr': how mundane. That is not valuable history; what is valuable is how people have used the infamy of this tweet (and now its lucrative sale) to reflect on the structures of our lives. It's prosaic to set up a Twitter account; it's fascinating to see how, 15 years later, people think about Twitter as part of their cultural heritage. To talk about money is a way of ascertaining value that isn't aligned with what

the object is: What are you buying if the thing is still available for free to everyone? Is it worth $2.9 million? Doesn't matter. But it's worth one thing, for sure: discussing.   *Orit Gat*

The phreaker
Florida, USA

In 1968, Joe Engressia was suspended from the University of South Florida and fined $25. He had been selling free long-distance phone calls for a $1 fee. The suspension became a media sensation, in no small part because of Engressia's extraordinary story. He was born blind and with a self-proclaimed IQ of 172. The telephone was his obsession. As a child, he would retreat into what he called 'the soft hum of the dial tone', exploring an entirely auditory world where sightlessness did not matter.

One day, after a disgruntled babysitter locked the phone dial, he learnt to call by rapidly tapping the hang-up switch. Not long after, he discovered something incredible: if he whistled into the phone at 2637.02Hz (Engressia had perfect pitch), he could trick the phone company into believing that he had hung up. But the line remained connected. He could

FIRST WORD SPOKEN ON A TELEPHONE

A cry of pain from engineer Antonio Meucci's patient who was being treated with a copper wire and electric shocks, 1856

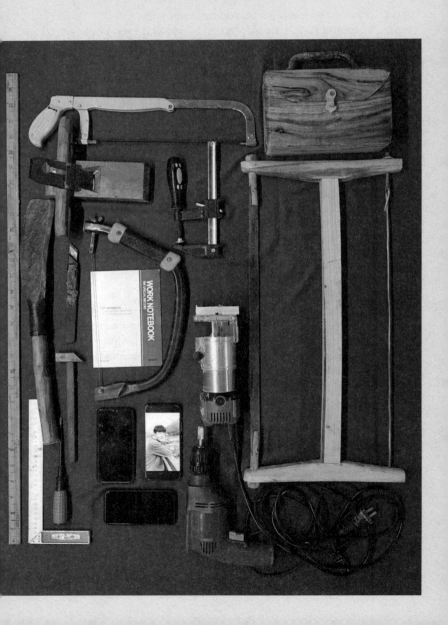

Weihan Chen   *Hi Xiaojie. Thank you for taking my call. Can you hear me?*
Shancun Xiaojie   Hello, yes I can.

WC   How many followers do you have right now?
SX   Including TikTok, Weibo, Tencent and Kwai, I have over 26 million.

WC   What kind of content do you share?
SX   I make short films about my life in Qi Peak Lin, a rural village in the province of Fujian in southeast China. Most of them involve me making things for my family or neighbours, from wood or bamboo. I've made a fan, a treadmill, a small car, a flush toilet for the village, a make-up box, an articulated dog…

WC   What made you become an influencer? What did you do before?
SX   I worked in town as a salesperson for an insurance company. After work I'd watch short videos – my favourites were low-quality vlogs, like one of someone putting mud on their body, or going scuba diving. The vloggers looked like they were having so much fun. I grew up in the countryside and I've always loved making things with primitive tools and materials. I realised no one was uploading anything like this so I decided to move back to the country and do it myself.

WC   And do you get paid for it?
SX   About 80 percent of my income comes from commercial work for brands. I recently did a campaign for Huawei. I also have my own brand selling agricultural products. And I do campaigns for charities: I help to market agricultural goods in different counties, and in my village I promote the products of local farmers on my Kwai platform.

WC   Do you feel pressured to fill your day with activities that get the most clicks?
SX   Not really. I film short videos of going to the mountains with my parents – this kind of video doesn't have as many clicks, but I keep posting it. I see TikTok as a way to record my life.

WC   What is your most clicked-on post?
SX   I made a wedding dress out of a mosquito net for my friend in the village. My 'couples' videos gain more clicks than others, so I make sure I do more of these.

Previous page   Portrait of his phone by Shancun Xiaojie

A PHONE CALL WITH SHANCUN XIAOJIE

WC   Do you mean the films of you and your girlfriend?
SX   It is storytelling. We don't say that we are boyfriend and girlfriend but people assume that we are. In the film my female friend will need something – like a pillow or a badminton racket – and I will make it for her out of stuff from the woods.

WC   Why do you think people like this material?
SX   Girls envy the girlfriend who has a wonderful boyfriend that can make everything for her. They think it is very sweet and they want that kind of boyfriend.

WC   How many takes do you do, and how long do you spend editing?
SX   I will shoot something twice, but not more. The simple stories take one day to edit and the complicated ones can take seven. The outcome is a one-minute film.

WC   What does your typical day look like?
SX   If I am working on a film I go from 7am to 6pm. I get materials in the morning, do the job in the afternoon and develop new ideas at night. If I am working for a brand on a campaign, I will commute the day before as I'm very remote – it takes three hours to get to the airport.

WC   Do you ever turn your phone off, or take a break?
SX   I have one or two days off a month and I don't take holidays. Once when I was upset, I gave myself a half-day break; I gave my friends notice by posting 'moments' on WeChat so that they didn't worry, then I put my phone way out of reach and found a quiet place.

WC   You champion a slower life in the countryside, but this all sounds quite fast paced.
SX   In many ways my life in the village is quite simple. But it took me a while to get used to being an influencer. A lot of people think that it is easy but this is not true. It was very stressful at the beginning.

WC   How many phones do you have?
SX   Two. One is for logging in to social media and communication, and one is just for filming – I can't have someone call me when I'm filming. I use an iPhone 12 for filming, which is faster and has a better camera. The capability of the phone is essential as sometimes I rely on it to live-stream.

WC   Is your phone important to you?
SX   My mobile is like a partner to me, it is like my co-worker, and I always take very good care of it. If my phone becomes hot while I'm using it, I will put it away to let it take a break. It is important to me not only physically but also mentally.

WC   Are mobile phones important to other people in your village?
SX   Yes. Before, the transmission of information was relatively slow, but now villagers use phones to synchronise with the city. They are no longer straggling behind. The phone is also crucial for e-commerce here. I teach villagers how to live-stream and film to promote their agricultural merchandise on short video platforms.

WC   Do you get worried that people will stop following you?
SX   When I reached 10 million followers I did, but now I don't think it will matter to me. I will do what I want to do and what I believe, no matter what. Living here in the mountains, I feel relaxed, chilled. Sometimes, when I walk alone or I'm doing farm work, I get the feeling I own the entire mountain.

The first transatlantic call from New York to London in 1927

then place a free call, anywhere in the world. Phreaking – the term coined to describe this kind of telecommunication system hacking – was born.

After Engressia was caught, he received calls from other phreaks who had arrived at the same revelations. Some did it using cassette tapes of an electric organ, whose tones resembled those of phone lines. Others created blue boxes, cigarette box-sized attachments that would allow you to play sounds into the phone. Many were teenagers; a sizeable number were blind.

The telephone network was the largest, widest-reaching machine of its day. By the 1960s, the US boasted 80 million lines. The telephone itself had become a mundane, everyday device. 'Imagine the rotary phone,' says phreaking historian Phil Lapsley, 'the most boring thing you can think of. The phreaks looked at it and said

"I want to know how it works." And once you do know how it works, "I wonder if you can make it do things it wasn't designed to do?"'

Phreaks looked for gaps to exploit. Eluding payment for calls was one of these. Another was the discovery that, in some areas, all callers shared engaged and wrong number signals. If you shouted into the handset you could freely converse with others, a sort of prototype conference call. There were joke lines, where dialling a certain number would lead to an answering machine sketch. Some phreaks played pranks: Engressia enjoyed connecting recent divorcees, or wiring a liquor store to a Mormon church, then listening to the fireworks that followed.

The most infamous phreaker of all – and the first to be imprisoned – was Captain Crunch, who took his name from a flute, given away for free

with Cap'n Crunch cereal, that replicated a 2600Hz tone (other phreak pseudonyms included Dr No, Peter Perpendicular Pimple and Regina Watts Towers). For Crunch, phreaking was serious. 'I do it for one reason and one reason only', he explained to the journalist Ron Rosenbaum, 'I'm learning about a system.' He worked out how to route a telephone call so that it circumnavigated the globe, bouncing through telephone exchanges in a stream of kerchings.

Phreaking's heyday was brief. Phone companies and the FBI ganged up to prosecute freeloaders. By the 80s, with phone companies automating their systems, cheating them became increasingly difficult. But it has a remarkable legacy. Numerous phreaks shifted from the phone to the computer, becoming developers, programmers and hackers, sometimes all three. 'Computer freaking,' Rosenbaum wrote, 'may be the wave of the future.' Nomenclature aside, he was spot on. Rosenbaum's *Esquire* article inspired a young Steve Wozniak to build blue boxes, who sold them through his friend Steve Jobs. 'If there had never been a blue box,' said Wozniak, 'there would have never been an Apple computer.'

Engressia abandoned phreaking after being arrested in 1971. For a stint he put his exploits to use as a troubleshooter for the Bell Telephone Company. He also ran *Stories and Stuff*, a sort of proto-podcast accessed by calling his number and listening to the answering machine. In 1988 he began to identify as a five-year-old child in an attempt to erase the abuse he had suffered at a Catholic school; soon

after, he legally changed his name to Joybubbles. When he died in 2007 from a heart attack, he was commemorated with a four-hour conference call.   *Joe Lloyd*

Independent dialling
Kansas, USA

Apple's platform monopoly is nothing new, in the world of telecommunications.

The fight for control of the phone system is as old as the phone itself. The Bell Telephone Company established by Alexander Graham Bell's father-in-law Gardiner Greene Hubbard controlled patents and rarely permitted the operation of third-party equipment on its network from the moment of its inception in 1877. Spare a thought then for Almon Strowger, who came to the telephone business accidentally. An undertaker in Kansas City, in 1891 he found he was losing business to a competitor whose telephone-operator wife kept routing calls away from Strowger to her husband's funeral home business. Strowger's complaints to AT&T (a

Early mobile use, the Iranian Embassy siege in London, 1980

subsidiary of Bell) went unanswered. His solution? To invent the stepping switch, an electromechanical device that switches an input signal path to one of several possible output paths, directed by a train of electrical pulses. The stepping switch enabled the automation of a telephone call. It put Strowger back in the funeral business and obviated the need for a telephone operator altogether.

The story continues in 1894 when an opportunity arose after Bell's first patent for telephones expired. By then criticism of AT&T had started to make the rounds. People complained about the company's exorbitant rates. An industry war between Bell and a group of scrappy insurgents ensued. Ordinary people, many from rural areas, started successful companies. There was Strowger and his Automatic Electric Company (subsequently part of the GTE Corporation, now Verizon) as well as Stromberg-Carlson, Kellogg, and American

Electric Throw Away Intercom. 'These independents were at once idealists and opportunists, activists and entrepreneurs,' writes Robert MacDougall, author of *The People's Network* (2013). 'They spoke of giving telephony back to the people.' And they did. By 1906, after little more than a decade, the independent telephone movement that built phones, switchboards, networks, controlled more than half of the six million telephones in the United States. *Anniina Koivu*

Koumpounophobia
California, USA

At key moments in the development of certain Apple products, it was intimated that Steve Jobs had a fear of buttons. Notably, the Apple CEO reacted with disgust to early iterations of the brand's first multi-button mouse. 'What morons have you working on this project?' he

barked at the staffer leading its development. The offending prototype was abandoned. In psychological terms, disgust and anger are broadly accepted as trigger responses to fear. This makes it easy to believe (if not hard to actually attribute) that such a specific and seemingly irrational fear may be responsible for innovations in touch screen technology, the trend towards uncluttered displays and the frictionless intimacy with which we interact with our personal tech devices.

Jobs never said on record that he feared buttons, but zipper-fly jeans and a roll-neck jumper is certainly the uniform of a man who resents fumbling with fastenings. In fact, the buttons we dress with are obsolete and long have been. Despite their status as slightly more convenient than a tie or hook-and-eye, the advent of zips and Velcro should have seen the button pop off. An innovator like Jobs may have found the passive acceptance of obsolete objects offensive. Others who admit to 'koumpounophobia' – a fear of buttons – list reactions that range from annoyance to extreme aversion. It's one thing to choose to dress oneself without buttons, but another to attempt to eradicate buttons from the world completely.

Perhaps the scariest button is the pretender button that has been added to a garment for style or affectation. It has no corresponding buttonhole and sits superficially, ready to catch on something. This kind of button should be feared because it is a thing without a function that pretends to be a thing with a function. It's a pseudo-skeuomorph, a sinecure, a sham.

If Steve Jobs was afraid of physical buttons, or the obsolescence or inauthenticity that they represent, it may account for why they were innovated out of Apple devices. This anecdote, if true, still doesn't totally explain why Jobs would then tolerate the push button-like interfaces of apps and tools that litter Apple operating systems: the icons on an iPhone home screen, for example. Perhaps, as psychologists inform us, the real fear is the loss of control. The only buttons that are allowed to remain are virtual, their image and function under the complete power of the programmer.   *Bryony Quinn*

The history of necromancy In the ether

Tupac's hologram performing on stage, Audrey Hepburn advertising chocolate on YouTube, Peter Cushing tyrannising rebel fighters in *Rogue One: A Star Wars Story...* These digital resurrections are just some of the latest examples of necromancy. The earliest written account of necromancy – the art of communing with or raising the dead

24

– goes back to around the eighth century BCE, when Odysseus, in Homer's *Odyssey*, seeks the advice of the dead prophet Tiresias to guide his voyage home. Odysseus's Nekyia ritual used the blood of sacrificed animals to mix libations favoured by ghosts. Flash forward almost 3,000 years and, on your phone, apps such as MyHeritage's Deep Nostalgia instead use machine learning to animate photographs of deceased loved ones, and companies like Microsoft promise to soon amalgamate emails, chat history and images to reincarnate a digital double of the dead for you to talk with, should you want to.

From blood to data, the means of communing with the dead has of course changed over time. But it was the invention of electricity – and then the phone – that, for a large part of modern Western history, would spur connections to the spirit world.

About 200 years ago, should you have wished to make contact with the spirit world, you might have sought the help of a medium – a woman who, through the ritual of a seance, channelled the voices of the dead. The rise of the medium as a conduit coincided with the burgeoning understanding of the science of electricity. Men of science confidently and gleefully declared that women, with their 'fragility', were simply victims of greater sensitivity to the vibrations of the electromagnetic ether which, by coincidence, also made them excellent conductors.

Early nineteenth-century experimenters in electricity such as Andrew Ure and Luigi Galvani

FIRST WORD TYPED ON THE INTERNET

LO (the system crashed before GIN could be entered)
by Charley Kline, 1969

had already 'proved' the connection between life force and electricity by crudely animating corpses, using currents. Telegraphy had also shown electricity's imperviousness to physical obstacles through the velocity at which messages were transmitted. It was therefore naturally assumed that electricity was a vital component of the ethereal milieu through which the afterlife might be contacted.

In the late nineteenth century, the invention of the telephone and also of Guglielmo Marconi's wireless radio provided the perfect opportunity to remove mediums – and women – from the equation. Here were devices that could reach across space and time to connect the world in greater fidelity than the telegraph, and also, surely, to the spirit world.

Immediately, the necromantic potential of these new telecommunications tools was eagerly explored by their inventors: Marconi believed that all voices were trapped in the electromagnetic ether, and in the 1920s worked on a device to resurrect the last words of Jesus Christ.

**FIRST PHOTO UPLOADED
ONTO THE WEB**

was of all-female parody pop group
Les Horribles Cernettes
by Tim Berners-Lee, 1992

Simultaneously, vigorous patent troll Thomas Edison, convinced that life itself was just physical matter in the ether needing to be correctly channelled, worked on the 'spirit phone', of which little remains save a semi-satirical piece in a 1921 *Literary Digest*. Alexander Graham Bell's phone was supposedly inspired by a pact he made with his younger brother, Edward, who died at age 19 in 1867, that the first one to die would attempt to contact the other. This was all with the support of his famed interlocutor and assistant Thomas Watson, himself a committed spiritualist. Even mediums experienced a brief renaissance during this period as 'phone-voyants' who could supposedly interpret the voices of the dead from the white noise of the line.

The phone – unlike telegraphy, mediums and blood sacrifice – stuck around and was increasingly augmented with an array of sensors to greater attune it to the ether: humanly imperceptible infrared sensors that can gauge distance with remarkable accuracy, microphones that hear beyond the range of human hearing, moisture sensors, thermometers and gyroscopes, all connected to vast amounts of processing power somewhere in a desert, became the latest and greatest in necromantic technology reaching out into the world beyond the human sensorium. We may look askance at the work of Bell, Edison, Watson, Marconi and others now, presuming their spiritualism to be at odds with the Western rationalism they epitomise. But will our own ambitions to capture, record, relive, reincarnate and recreate through our smartphone conduits be viewed any differently? The uncanny relationship of our selves to our tele-presence channelled through our phones continues to evolve – so it seems necromancy will always be the killer app.   *Tobias Revell*

An Open University student working on the phone, c 1988

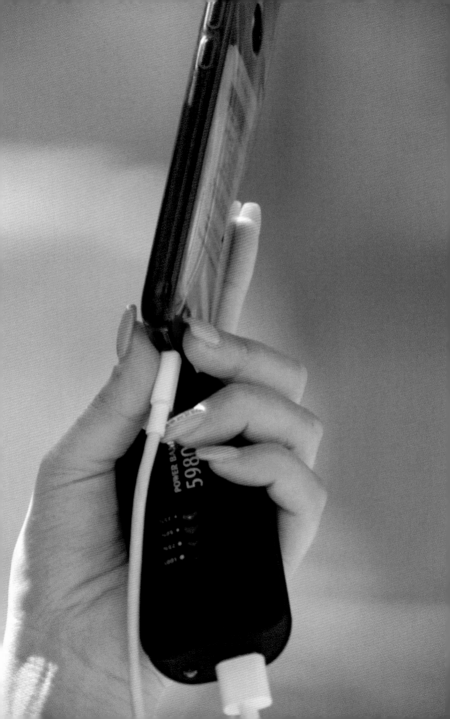

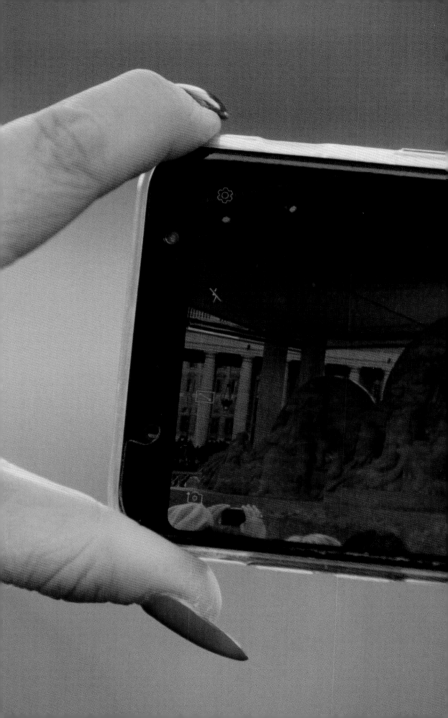

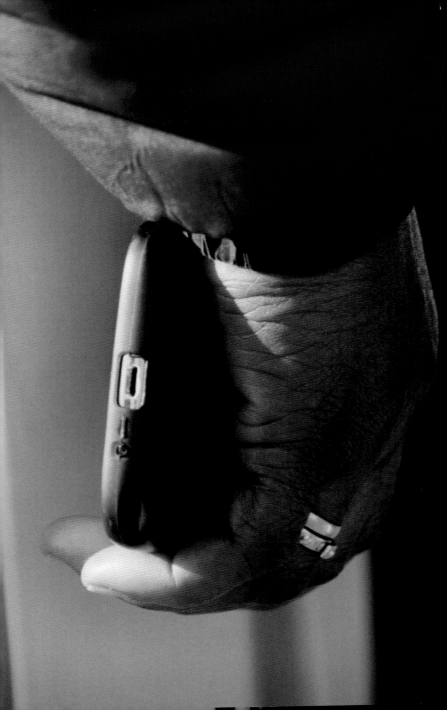

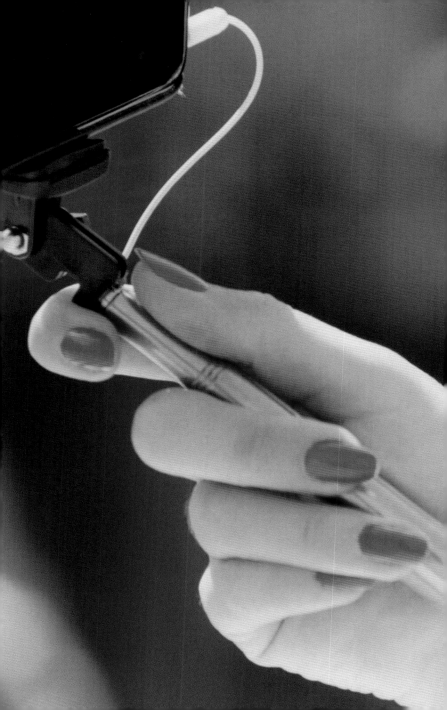

TELL ME, DO YOU INTEND
TO FUCK IT?

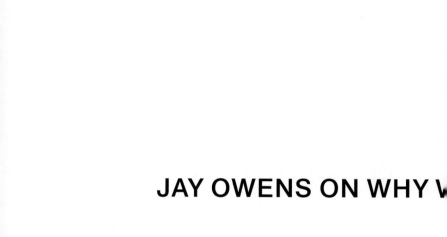
JAY OWENS ON WHY W

ALL THE IPHONE SEXY

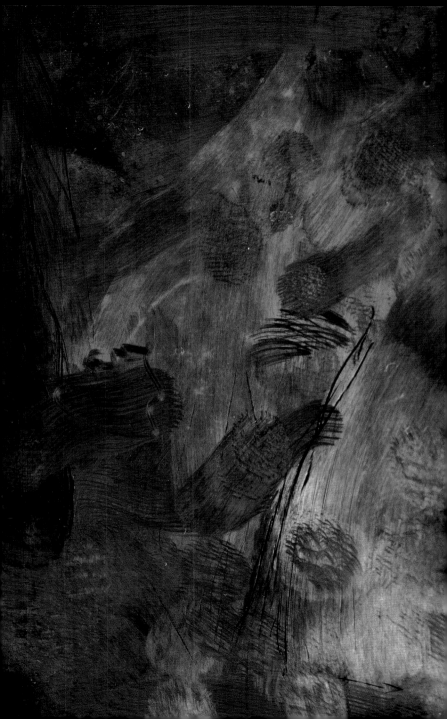

APPLE

People still call the iPhone 'sexy'. Not only tech dudes or horny teenagers but ordinary people. In tweets and reviews, Reddit posts and YouTube videos, thousands make this absurd statement every year. The iPhone's colours are sexy, the quality of its camera is sexy and so is the speed of its battery charging. Quality is sexy. Being a newer, more recent model is sexy.

This shouldn't be happening. The iPhone is a six-inch hunk of precision-engineered glass, aluminium and rare earth metals: it's not a person, or a body. In 2011, journalist Mat Honan wrote a vigorous polemic on Gizmodo against calling gadgets 'sexy' at all. 'Tell me, do you intend to fuck it?' It's lazy writing, he argues: 'those writing it almost never mean it. When a writer unleashes "sexy", more often than not what is meant is "desirable."'

But the fans don't agree. Apple launched the iPhone 12 in autumn 2020 to rapturous feedback on Twitter that it is 'sexy af'. And everyone seems to know what they mean.

So I want to take this statement seriously. What might the intensity and eroticism of this desire for an inanimate device reveal about us, and what we want from technology?

●

An enormous part of contemporary erotic life passes through the smartphone. It can feel as though it's impossible to get a date without being on dating apps; we have agreed, it would seem, that this is the proper theatre for desire to be explored. Physical gestures of flirtation – the smiles and eyebrow raises; the coy turns of the head; the way two people will mirror each other's body language – are instead performed on our phones. We caress our screens – scrolling, flicking, pausing – our fingers dancing with animation, when conversation is going well.

Critic Huw Lemmey described smartphones to me in an email as 'sexual prostheses… Suddenly a world of flirtation, sex chat and arranging hookups [has] been enabled in all sorts of places,' he says. 'For so many people a phone is not just for communication but maybe an interactive masturbatory aid; you take to bed your vibrator and the guy you matched with on Tinder, who [you] might never meet but has good sex chat.'

If a relationship does form, the smartphone continues to be central. Sexting, once the source of so much moral panic around

Images throughout Stéphanie Saadé, details of *Digiprints*, 2018–2020

young people, is slowly becoming recognised as a normal part of sexual behaviour and identity formation. Technology can enhance pleasure. Many will be familiar with the delicious jolt of receiving nudes on the encrypted messaging app Signal: the shock of an unexpected erotic energy that can be set to vanish as suddenly as it arrives. FaceTime and WhatsApp have probably kept more long-distance relationships alive during the past year than any other technologies.

Is there a kind of contagion, a symbolic slippage in which the libidinal energy channelled through the iPhone means that the device comes to acquire some sexy qualities itself?

Given the incessant use of 'sexy' in online discussion about the iPhone, and mindful of Rule 34 of the internet – 'If it exists, there is porn of it' – I had assumed some explicitly sexual relationship to the technology would exist. Yet Pornhub did not oblige, and I browsed kink social network FetLife in vain. Discussion on the Apple forum among groups 'Riggers and Ropesluts' and 'Poly and Kinky' was disappointingly prosaic: 'iPhone 6 Settings help needed'; or 'How can I make my iPhone XS Max talk to my Apple Watch?' Eight people listed 'Being whipped by an iPhone' as an interest; seven were 'curious' about 'Being more important than a damn iPhone.' That was about it. I asked a couple of techno-fetishists of my acquaintance if I was missing anything, but they agreed: iPhones don't seem to be a direct turn-on.

This was unexpected because phones are such deeply tactile things. Apple Screen Time informs me that I pick up my iPhone X 45 times a day; no wonder irreverent UK tech site The Register has christened phones 'fondle slabs'. Our phones are not simply media devices or transparent conduits for the vast amount and variety of information that passes through them; instead, they have a tactile fascination as objects in themselves.

How can we understand this desire for an inanimate device? Perhaps the iPhone is, as Paris Hilton once memorably described herself, 'sexy but not sexual': rich with sexual association and allusion, but always at a remove. It teases the promise of sex but cannot deliver: there is a level of human, embodied sensuality where it falls short.

We might first try to understand the iPhone's sexiness through the commercial magic of the brand: that marketing sleight of hand in which commodities come to be invested with human values.

Scott Galloway, professor of marketing at New York University Stern School of Business, would surely agree the iPhone is sexy. According to his 2017 book *The Four: The Hidden DNA of Amazon, Apple, Facebook and Google*, Apple's defining brand value is luxury, and luxury comes down to sex: 'It combines our instinctive need to transcend the human condition and feel closer to divine perfection, with our desire to be more attractive to potential mates.' Historically, luxury was expressed in the soaring vaulted ceilings and dazzling stained glass of a cathedral; now, luxury is in a piece of technology so perfect that it seems human hands cannot possibly have created it. Luxury is the market equivalent of feathers on a bird. It's irrational and sexual, and it easily overwhelms the killjoy, rational signals of the brain. 'I just had to have it,' said one fan, reacting to the ostentatiously perfect surface of the gloss black iPhone 7. 'Is there something wrong with me?' asked another.

No. And as Apple's marketing material demonstrates, this is no accident. iPhone adverts are strange: they make the phone a body. They borrow a visual language less from sci-fi or action movies than from erotica. Devices are shot in extreme close-up, almost always dimly lit. A beam of light traces across a surface so smooth that it occupies a space somewhere between highly touched-up video and pure digital render. The light traces the edges of the device and slowly circles its curves. It's a kind of strip-tease, a game of concealment and partial reveal, an art house movie sequence with sunlight filtering through the slats of a blind and playing across a woman's naked body.

It's curious to want to call an advert 'objectifying', because of course it is: its function is to promote an object. Yet this none-theless feels like the right word, not only in reference to the object of the ad's intentions, but the kind of gaze that is filming it. The camera, the eye, is fixated on the phone's 'thing-ness': not what it can do, but the object's physical, material presence in itself. In order to make the iPhone a luxury good – to justify its higher selling price and maintain Apple's 38 percent margins – it needs to assert craftsmanship and provenance. And so the adverts go on and on, far more than you might think the ordinary consumer cares, about the materials and manufacture of the device. The iPhone 7 advert had detail shots of an Apple logo being laser-etched in glass; the camera housing being drilled out from the aluminium body; plus 70 seconds on 'a whole new process to achieve a high gloss

black finish'. The webpage for the iPhone 12 Pro shows liquids splashing across the device in luxurious slow motion. The gloss is, as ever, unreal. These are the aesthetics of latex, of fetishwear. One starts to wonder if it might be deliberate.

According to Hannes Hacke, co-curator of the 2018 exhibition *Erotik der Dinge* [The Eroticism of Things] at Berlin's Museum of Things, two of the ways in which objects can have an erotic quality are 'through shape and materiality'. The items Hacke and colleagues presented at the exhibition ranged from vibrators to used sneakers, a glass chandelier, even an aubergine. Often the objects 'resemble[d] the bodily form or more precisely genitals, breasts, penises, vulvas, buttocks,' Hacke says. 'Not [the] depiction of a body part, but more the resemblance.'

The curators asked if 'a sharp object could be an erotic object – or a square object or something that is not round, or that does not have a smooth texture?' It seemed that the answer was generally no: curves were essential. And indeed curves have distinguished the Apple brand for decades, from the colourful jelly forms of the 1998 iMac desktop computer to the 'consistent edge radius and border size' of the iPhone X that its Reddit fans so admired. These aluminium and glass contours may be a considerable distance from the organic forms of the human body, but nonetheless there's shared DNA: Apple is, somehow, more organic than other tech brands. This most abstract of bodily resemblances is part of where its sexiness originates.

The exhibition included a Sensing Materials Lab, where visitors were asked to squeeze and fondle a series of materials and map them from non-sexy to sexy. Rankings varied enormously from one person to the next, but one group of materials were consistently among the sexiest: 'rubber, silicone and wet materials like gels', confirms design researcher Lilo Viehweg who co-created the lab, 'like, somehow, skin or body-related materials.'

Yet an actual body-mimicking iPhone is disgusting – as designer/technologist Marc Teyssier found with his Skin On interface. Because 'human skin is the best interface for interaction', he and the Bristol Interaction Group created artificial skin as a new gestural control interface that could be interacted with through pinching, prodding and tickling. But this digital epidermis – a greyish Caucasian colour in tone, skin-textured, with the odd hair – falls right into that

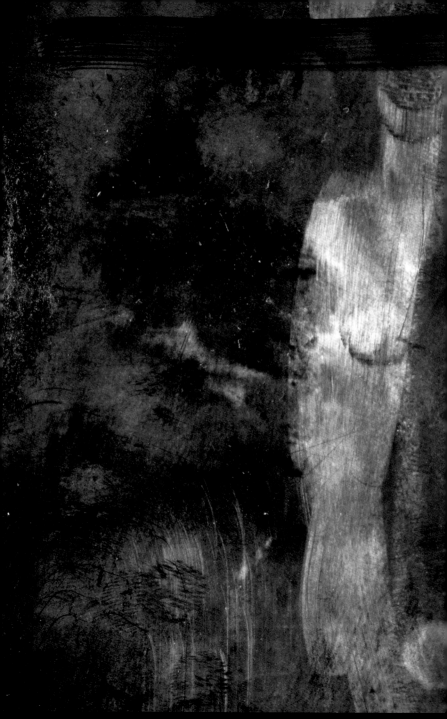

uncanny valley between artificial and real, and as such reads as far
more disgusting than desirable. Nonetheless, smartphones remain
intensely skin-like on a metaphorical level: we stroke, and they are
minutely responsive. Our fingertips enjoy the ultra-smoothness
of their Gorilla Glass screens, velvety like a youthful cheek. Silicone
cases add a body-equivalent degree of friction.

'From the classical (and even the cybernetic) viewpoint, technology
is an extension of the body,' the philosopher Jean Baudrillard wrote
in 1976. Baudrillard was discussing JG Ballard's *Crash* (1973),
a book the author described as the first 'pornographic novel about
technology'. A group of alienated former car-crash victims cruise
the motorways and flyovers of suburban northwest London, seeking
to re-enact celebrity motor accidents in order to experience 'a new
sexuality, born from a perverse technology'. The book is a blur
of monotonous mechanical imagery and equally objectified bodies,
sexuality distilled down to figures and resemblances, forms and
angles. Characters consider the possibilities of making love to a car
exhaust, an ashtray, 'the angle between two walls'. The idea that
something as abstract as the iPhone body's geometry might be 'sexy'
is a concept entirely of this world.

    Crash is the Freudian death drive – a compulsion to repeat –
made crudely literal. Driving kills thousands every year, the consequences of error could not be more real, and yet people slow down
to gawp at car crashes as though watching an action movie on screen.
Risk is a thrill. Ballard's defamiliarisation is asking us only to see
what it is that we do. What if the iPhone's sexiness lies in the immi-
nent possibility of disaster it contains? Perfection's allure lies in
its fragility: smoothness is only sexy because we know how easily
it could be smashed.

    An account of the iPhone's materiality must not gloss over
the violence of its origins. Perfection is built from minerals mined
in conflict zones by sometimes underage or indentured labour, the
waste rock polluting waterways and sickening local communities.
The geopolitics of the twenty-first century is being shaped by this
demand for rare earth metals, as mineral deposits are found and
fought over on new Arctic frontiers. Aluminium cases are polished
to smoothness in factories full of dust, irritating workers' lungs and

risking explosion. Once in users' hands, ever-larger screens make ever-greater energy demands: each map search, Instagram scroll or email download pulls data from cloud servers around the planet, kept cool by humming air conditioning units. Data centres use two percent of the world's total electricity generation. Come the end of their lives, only one percent of smartphones will be recycled, generating further inequalities and health hazards. The rest sit, inanimate, in cupboards and drawers, until they're binned.

The iPhone's sexiness is created through violence and destruction. It is *reliant* on its wastefulness. And this is a pillar of Apple's brand strategy.

One of the ways the iPhone remains materially perfect – and therefore a luxury good – is through Apple's repair restrictions. Go to a non-authorised repair shop and your warranty is void. But staying within the Apple system is vastly expensive (a screen repair on the largest phones costs £316.44), leading people to decide it's easier to get a new gadget rather than to fix it. The Right to Repair movement is fighting for change, but Apple spends millions lobbying against it, and also resists through the phone's design: the iPhone 12 is programmed so that, if third-party technicians swap out a broken camera or battery, the entire device is disabled. Rapid obsolescence is built in. This is obscene.

Scott Galloway may have described luxury as a closeness to perfection that brings us closer to God, but the vision of the sacred here is surely closer to notorious philosopher of the perverse, Georges Bataille. For Bataille, luxury operates, according to his 1949 book of the same name, as the 'accursed share', an excess of energy that 'must necessarily be lost without profit; it must be spent, willingly or not, gloriously or catastrophically.' This excess is, he believed, inherent to both eroticism and economy, in fact to life itself: it is integral to the condition of living on a planet powered by an endlessly exploding sun.

'All is inverted,' says Baudrillard, as if in agreement. 'Here it is the Accident' – in Ballard's work, a car crash; for us, the shattered phone screen – 'which gives life its very form; it is the Accident, the irrational, which is *the sex of life*.'

Where can we possibly go from here?

Some may wish to argue against all this capitalist obscenity, to argue instead for virtue. Might we imagine the 'good phone',

second-hand and 10 years old, repaired and upgraded? Perhaps it's even more ethical if the phone's user experience *isn't* smooth and *isn't* very enjoyable. Some say they desire a device that discourages them from using it, and incentivises them to disconnect. But this is the masochism of the saints. It may do it for some but I fear it lacks mass appeal.

Instead, perhaps we might be liberated from this techno-perversion by the progression of technology itself.

The ability of the iPhone to sense is now what makes it sexy, philosopher Timothy Secret told me:

> *While the iPhone was always sexy as a black mirror, a smooth monolith on its exclusive pedestal, what's interesting to me is that it's now developed a kind of intimacy that it didn't have before that emerges particularly with FaceID and Raise to Wake. I look at it, it looks at me, there is this slight microsecond of lag as it works to recognise me in which I feel some anxiety, and then it opens up by mere eye contact to tell me personal notifications that it wouldn't tell anyone else, and I feel the satisfaction of being recognised, trusted by it, flooding in.*

Through this interaction, the iPhone becomes sexy in the way of 'a therapist who you've disclosed everything to, who you fantasise knows you better than yourself,' Secret continued. 'Ultimately it's not that you desire the phone but that you fantasise the phone desires you.' As Siri's predictive capacities increase, there is the prospect that the phone is no longer a sex object but something more, 'our deepest confidant, our best friend.'

Perhaps desire will eventually be numbed, as in the marital bed, by closeness and familiarity. Perhaps this material eroticism of technology is but an immature, youthful stage of our relationship with these machines. Eroticism demands difference, sex therapists such as Esther Perel tell us: 'It thrives on the mysterious, the novel, and the unexpected.' It requires distance, a 'space between the self and the other'. When predictive technologies appear to read our minds and know our wishes before we do, that distance is gone. They become our best friends. They will become, eventually, our selves.

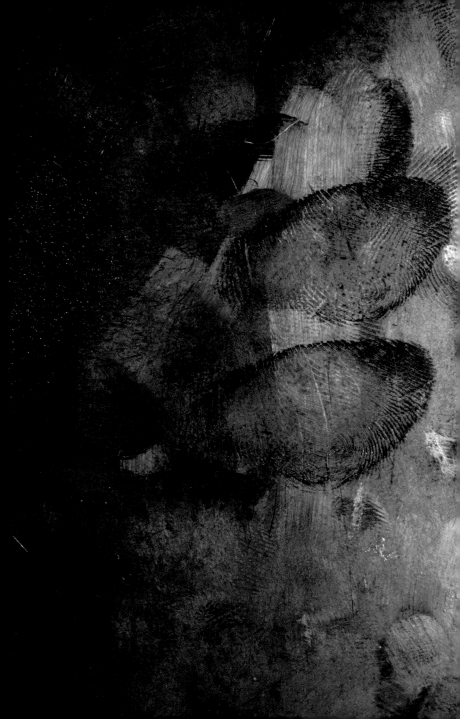

BOOM BAP BOOM
BAP BOOM BAP

AJAY HOTHI ON

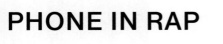

PHONE IN RAP

NOKIA
5110

Freedom of expression.

The Nokia 5110 lets you express yourself instantly. Simply click off one coloured Xpress-on™ Cover, then click on a new one – it's really that easy. Change your mind, click over to the colour of your choice with some exciting options free* instore to try for yourself. There are seven sophisticated metallic Xpress-on™ Covers to choose from too, including Antiqua Red, Shark Silver and Tango Orange. All this from a phone with outstanding talk and standby times, and the Nokia Navi™ Key; one simple-to-use key which controls everything. Yet the new Nokia 5110 is smaller and lighter than you'd ever expect. Call 0990 003110 today for a leaflet.

NOKIA
CONNECTING PEOPLE

Nokia 5110 mobile phone ad, 1998

I got a raw deal   so I'm goin' for the steel
'Black Steel in the Hour of Chaos'   Public Enemy   1988

The track 'Black Steel in the Hour of Chaos', released on the Def Jam record label, is a telephone conversation between Public Enemy band members Chuck D, who is planning a breakout from prison, and Flava Flav, who offers words of encouragement. Flav recorded his lines from the studio using the telephone mic while producer Hank Shocklee taped the voice coming through the speaker phone from the studio next door.

Shocklee wanted to filter the fundamentals of rap through a sound developed by Def Jam founder Rick Rubin to create a genre of Black music that was commercial yet era-defining in its social commentary. Rubin had recorded grunge-psychedelia-noise band Hose onto tape through a microphone plugged into a boombox. It sounded raw and flat. He harnessed what he learned from fringe punk-esque rock as Def Jam Recordings shifted towards the nascent rap scene. Emulating a guitar riff, his new rap sound – called boom bap – was stripped of warmth and reverb. It was replayed through an acoustic drum loop which was then broken up and replayed again through a sampler. The heavily mediated result was less dense than jazz, soul or reggae. It was of poor quality, atonal and anti-musical. By the mid-1980s, Def Jam had expanded rap beyond the vernacular of the Bronx and South Queens and given it its commercial sound.

In 'Black Steel in the Hour of Chaos' Shocklee revisited this sound through the symbolism of the telephone and the acoustics it enabled. Usually a high-pitched tenor, Flav's voice became scratchy and abrasive as if we were listening to the devil on Chuck D's shoulder, providing him with the guidance and direction needed to fight the powers that kept the Black man in America in his place, either in the army or prison. With the help of the telephone, Public Enemy became the progenitor of a new genre: gangsta rap.

$

There we go again,   I got a beep   The girl got nosy
beggin' for a peep   'Beepers'   Sir Mix-a-Lot   1989

Public Enemy's experiment was the first of rap's many flirtations with the sounds, symbols and habits associated with the phone. As the genre developed, the phone became a recurring instrument,

signalling alienation, a means of control or even the opportunity for financial freedom.

While Public Enemy were imploring their listeners to extricate themselves from the shackles that society's dominant institutions place on Black men, another form of rap celebrated upward mobility through emerging telecommunications.

With his ostentatious bling, Sir Mix-a-Lot drives down the LA highway in an open-topped Mercedes Benz, steering wheel in one hand and beeper in the other. In the video for 'Beepers', he describes getting pages in his limo while the girl in the passenger seat wants to know who from. He tells her the page is work-related before revealing to the listener that it's really another local girl wanting to hook up. He silences his prying companion by putting the vibrating pager in her panties.

Once predominantly the preserve of every emergency room doctor, by the late 1980s the beeper or pager had become the go-to accessory for street business, for hustlers working benzos or booty. After all, it made the city a man's boardroom. He was no longer tied down; the beeper afforded him a direct line to both entrepreneurial and sexual opportunities, and the image that Sir Mix-a-Lot projected was of both a player and a playboy, a pimp rolling with multiple ladies in between business deals.

$

Get paged by a G   or a business pal,
my shit is overflowin'
They won't allow   another page
'Skypager' A Tribe Called Quest   1991

In his essay '"Do you know the importance of a Skypager?": Telecommunications, African Americans, and Popular Culture' (2006), Davin Heckman claims the pager was key to allowing young African Americans a chance at socio-economic ascent. He argues that late twentieth-century technology afforded them business opportunities outside the traditional institutions from which they found themselves barred.

Perhaps because of the mobility facilitated by the beeper, by 1991 A Tribe Called Quest were able to position themselves in opposition to gangsta rap, both musically and image-wise. Members Q-Tip, Phife Dawg, Ali Shaheed Muhammad and Jarobi White

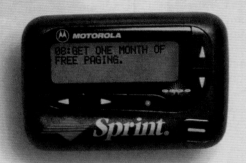

Unlimited paging.

Limited offer.

Sprint introduces unlimited paging for a single monthly lease rate.
Just give us a call and your pre-activated pager is on the way. And if you call
soon, we'll even include the first month for free. It's just that simple.

1-800-4-PAGERS

Motorola Sprint pager ad, 1996

claimed more influence from the sophisticated artistry of Black jazz and soul than from the boom bap slap of street rap. And the image they promoted of themselves was more cultured. In 'Skypager', Q-Tip raps about sipping wine and 'eating cacciatore with a twist of lime'.

Such was the street credibility of the pager combined with the commercial success of rap that by 1997, broadcaster MTV had launched its own pager network to its predominantly teenage audience. Several times a month, MTV would send out a toll-free number which recipients could call to hear details of competitions, promotions, giveaways, programme information and music news – a newsletter for the impending information age. The MTV pager network came complete with designer pagers by Motorola: the Liquid in blue, the Carbon in grey and the Outrageous in chartreuse.

$

A hundred thousand dollar bribe paid the bond for me
I copped a plea, [indecipherable],
they said could set me free   You have one minute remaining
'Intro Live from Fulton County Jail HD'
Gucci Mane   2010

After mainstream rap became dominated by stories of poverty told by multimillionaires, with slick, Hollywood-style production values, trap – a reference to 'trap houses', aka drug dens – was a form of rap music with a focus on synth backing tracks, hi-hat drums, sporadic hard bass and violent lyrical content. It was a return to rap's – and the rapper's – marginalised roots. One of trap's most successful exponents, Gucci Mane recorded a series of songs for his 2010 album *Burrrprint 2 (HD)* over the phone from jail while serving a year for parole violations. In doing so, he elaborated on Public Enemy's sentiment 20 years earlier, and the many rap artists since who wanted to authenticate their outlaw image by 'phoning it in'. These include Mac Dre, who in 1992 recorded the *Back n da Hood* EP while incarcerated for conspiracy to commit bank robbery, and Prodigy from rap group Mobb Deep, who in 2010 recorded 'The Phone Tap (Welcome to State Prison)' after being arrested for illegal possession of a firearm. X-Raided also recorded his album *Xorcist* in 1995 over the phone from jail. 'I'm much more creative in here,'

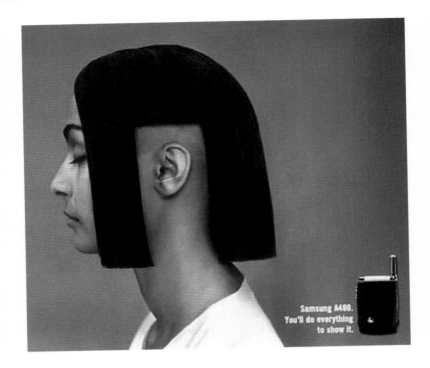

Samsung A400 mobile phone ad, 2000

the rapper told *Vibe* magazine in 1998. In all of these, the atonal, anti-musical sound amounted to an aural reproach to multi-millionaire rappers who were seen to have sanitised rap, or to have taken it from its roots on the fringes of society and made it fit for pop consumption.

$

Y'all on the 'Gram holdin' money to your ear
There's a disconnect   we don't call that money over here
'The Story of OJ'   Jay-Z   2017

Rapper-turned-entrepreneur Jay-Z's 'The Story of OJ' refers to the 'money phone' selfie: the Instagram trend which likely began when rapper 50 Cent, in collaboration with boxer Floyd Mayweather, set up promotions company The Money Team in 2011. The selfie featured a rapper holding a stack of cash up to his ear like a cell phone. Six years later, Jay-Z railed against this social-media image. For him, this ostentatious act was a puerile display. In response, a host of rappers castigated Jay-Z for patronising the very community that made him a household name, the general theme being that if they had the money, it was theirs to show off.

Pariah or not, Jay-Z's wealth and business success had by this time elevated the artist to a position of considerable influence, in part because of telecommunications. In 2013, he became one of the first rap artists to distribute his music via an app. Korean telecoms giant Samsung paid $5 million, as part of a total $20 million deal, to share his album *Magna Carta Holy Grail* (2013) for free with one million owners of the Galaxy S III, S4 and Note II, 72 hours before the record dropped in stores.

The music industry voiced concern that Jay-Z was bucking the system and would immediately be awarded a platinum record rather than wait the required 30 days to have sales counted and verified; and that he would receive a larger royalty share than contracted for. Almost immediately after launch, however, the app crashed due to over-demand. No matter: within minutes the record was available via torrents and peer-to-peer sharing networks, meaning the only people without access to it were record store owners. Jay-Z, like Sir Mix-a-Lot and A Tribe Called Quest before him, saw the cell phone for what it was: a business opportunity, rather than a musical one.

$

**Passive aggressive when we're texting
I feel the distance
'From Time'   Drake   2013**

Sex, control and cell phones sum up Drake's lyrical content.
In 2015, *Slate* magazine wrote that the Canadian rapper/singer/
actor/producer/businessman could claim 'the laurels of the 21st-
century bard of telephony' because the cell phone often provides
the cipher through which he conducts his relationships.

His track 'Star67' (2015), named for the pre-dial code that
hides your number from the recipient, details how he screens his
calls or lets his hook-ups hang on a message he knows they know
he has seen but has left unanswered.

Drake's passive-aggressive mobile phone etiquette lays
the foundations for his on-stage persona of the 'poor little rich
boy' who loves too much but is too heartbroken to be truly able
to accept love.

$

**And I know when that hotline bling
That can only mean one thing
'Hotline Bling'   Drake   2015**

Never has Drake's habit of reverting to the phone as a means of
amplifying distance rather than reducing it been more apparent than
in his most famous song, 'Hotline Bling'. It is aimed at a former
hook-up who used to booty-call the rapper when they both lived in
the same city. He has heard stories that without his supportive guidance, she is no longer 'a good girl'. Ever since he left town, he sings,
'you started wearing less and goin' out more... hangin' with some
girls I've never seen before... bendin' over backwards for someone
else... doing things I taught you, gettin' nasty for someone else'.

Speculation has it that Drake wrote 'Hotline Bling' about old
flame Zineb Samir. Whatever the case, while he addresses the
unnamed woman directly, there's no dialogue. Drake instead only
delivers a steady stream of assertions about her behaviour since they
broke up. The song is narrated as though he is leaving her a voice-
mail, perhaps even while scrolling through her Instagram feed.
Drake uses the phone simply to issue moral judgement from afar.

$

If you're calling to beg for some shit in general   press 4
'Cel U Lar Device'   Erykah Badu   2015

Erykah Badu sang '(You used to call me on my) Cel U Lar Device' to the same melody as 'Hotline Bling' a few months after the release of Drake's hit. The song formed part of her cell phone-themed song collection, the 2015 EP *But You Caint Use My Phone*, which, according to Jayson Greene in *Pitchfork* magazine, shares the themes of 'missed connections, call waiting, [and] answering machines'.

Badu's musical riposte shows her allegiance to the oral tradition of the blues, in which the emphasis is on the expression or repetition of the words rather than on the words themselves. 'Cel U Lar Device' essentially retains the lyric of 'Hotline Bling', but substitutes 'he' for 'she', after which Badu inserts an interlude in which the listener reaches the 'Erykah Badu hotline'.

This plays off Drake's 'Hotline Bling' and the voice message for his former lover. The caller isn't even given the opportunity to record a message and instead has to navigate imaginary numbered options. The power artists like Drake and Sir Mix-a-Lot attempt to wield over the opposite sex through the cell phone is negated. Badu uses the technology to shut down any attempt at contact.

$

I think you better call Tyrone   'Tyrone'   Erykah Badu   1997

Perhaps the last word on rap's engagement with the phone should go to Badu, in a song recorded around the time that the mobile phone became a must-have accessory. The story goes that 'Tyrone' was improvised live on stage. In 'Tyrone', the audience is present as Badu breaks up with her boyfriend (rumoured to be OutKast's André 3000) over the phone. She tells him he had better call his friend Tyrone to collect him and his things because she's kicking him out.

Badu has stated that women loved 'Tyrone' but men hated it, and she was accused of male-bashing. She was defiant in its defence. The song challenges future Tyrones, these men who since the early days of mobile telecommunications have used the phone not necessarily to connect, but to orchestrate gain – of money, sex and control. She reclaims the phone as an instrument of power – and there is no way he is using hers to make that final call.

10 GIGABITS PER SECOND,
100 TIMES FASTER,
ON A DIFFERENT
WAVELENGTH…

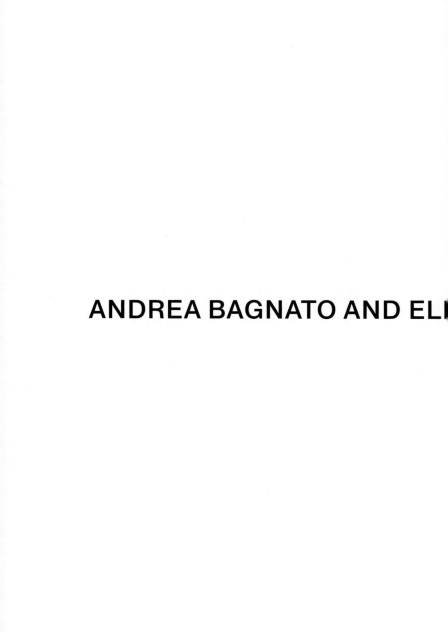

ANDREA BAGNATO AND ELI

IULIANO ON 5G IN MATERA

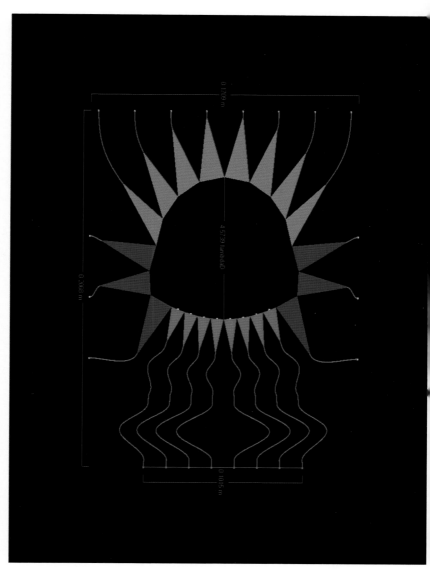

Images throughout Visualisations generated by Remcom's 5G and MIMO simulation software. They demonstrate new technologies, such as multiple-input, multiple-output (MIMO) and beamforming, higher frequency bands including millimetre waves, and changes to how base stations and devices are deployed and used.

Viale Carlo Levi runs along the southern edge of Matera, southern Italy, in a part of the city tourists rarely visit. On one side, the road flanks housing blocks built in the 1960s for residents who were displaced from the ancient city centre, called *Sassi* ('stones'). On the other, the horizon opens onto the Bradano river valley below and the Pollino mountains further away. The road is named after the anti-fascist intellectual who, because of his political convictions, was exiled to a small village in the region. His classic 1945 memoir *Christ Stopped at Eboli* revealed the conditions of Matera to postwar Italy. Levi wrote the city as an open-air inferno where cave-dwelling children died of malaria by the dozen. Little did it matter that the *Sassi* had evolved over hundreds of years into a unique, complex urban system, and that Matera had become impoverished only very recently; Levi's portrayal struck a chord with a country eager to stand comparison to the rest of Western Europe, and in 1952 the Italian parliament passed a 'special law' forcing all the *Sassi* inhabitants to move into new public housing.

It was on Levi's namesake road that on March 5, 2018, the first 5G base station was switched on, as part of a national plan to test the new mobile technology. Matera was chosen by the Italian government on the grounds that it was to be the next European Capital of Culture (the other test cities were Milan, Prato and Bari, selected for their geographical location, and L'Aquila, destroyed by an earthquake in 2009 and only partially rebuilt). An inconspicuous object – a one-metre-long grey box, bolted onto a crowded telecommunications mast – the Huawei-built 5G base station stood out for being the first in Italy, and one of the first in Europe. While we tend to think of mobile base stations as giant visible structures, the majority are concealed under various architectural details: inside fake chimneys, or behind billboards. Operating on the 3.7–3.8 GHz frequency bands, as opposed to the 800–1900 Mhz bands used by mobile phones all the way up to 4G, 5G networks promise much faster connections. But there is a trade-off: higher frequency means shorter wavelength, and thus reduced range. Increased speed comes at the price of a much higher density of base stations.

When 5G arrived in Matera, there was no question, in the eyes of the national government, local politicians or the telecommunications companies, that more speed was a desirable goal. From 2017 the local paper, *La Gazzetta del Mezzogiorno*, ran near-daily stories on the benefits 5G could bring to the city: the faster network would encourage new businesses to move in, helping to develop rural areas.

It could assist healthcare, by allowing for remote diagnosis; cultural institutions, by enabling VR and AR interfaces; and police forces, by facilitating drone surveillance and facial recognition. It could even help the local utility company reduce water leaks. In one of the articles, Matera's mayor expressed a vision in which the Capital of Culture designation, 5G technology and special economic zones could attract investment that would redeem not just the city but the entire Italian South. At a conference in Matera on May 22, local civil servants and entrepreneurs spoke of a 'fourth industrial revolution' and of data being 'the new oil'.

It was a surprise to many, then, that a year after the base station was installed, a local MP tabled a question in parliament about the possible health risks of 5G technology. From then on, the tone of newspaper coverage gradually shifted, with alarm taking the place of techno-optimism. The arguments echoed those of 5G opponents worldwide: that the effects of the 'new' wavelength (which is, in fact, close to domestic Wi-Fi) on the human body are under-researched, and more base stations would mean increased exposure to radio-frequency (RF) radiation.

Scepticism mounted until, on May 13, 2019, the first of many public demonstrations took place in Matera's main square, asking for the 5G base station to be switched off. A Stop 5G coalition developed and, on July 23, the mayor of neighbouring Scanzano Jonico issued an official order prohibiting the installation of 5G equipment within the boundaries of his municipality. By the end of 2019, over 30 cities – all along the peninsula – followed the example set by Scanzano Jonico, issuing anti-5G orders. In early 2020, conspiracy theories that associated 5G networks with Covid-19 transmission started spreading worldwide. As a result, the number of Italian mayors banning 5G rose to nearly 500, representing such large cities as Udine and Siracusa. This legislative form of opposition contrasts curiously with that in northern Europe, where countries like the UK and France have witnessed dozens of arson attacks against 5G masts.

In Matera, the anti-5G constituency is a heterogeneous bunch. Spearheaded by Salvatore De Bonis, both a populist MP and a landlord for whom the stakes appear to be a mix of political consensus and entrepreneurial self-interest, it includes individuals but also parents' associations and environmentalist groups. Over the past year, the positions of the Comitato Stop 5G Matera seem to have shifted from a moderate distrust of corporate interests to flat-out conspiracy theory.

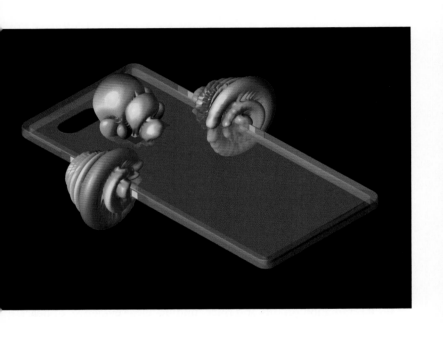

But what of the evidence? The question whether 5G can pose a danger to human health is a textbook example of socially disputed science. The scientific community broadly accepts that RF radiation is at once potentially harmful – which is why there are national and supranationally mandated limits – but safe at normal use levels, even if what constitutes 'normal use' is a point of contention. It doesn't help that up-to-date, independent scientific evidence is particularly hard to come by.

In 2011, a working group of the International Agency for Research on Cancer (IARC) of the World Health Organization (WHO) classified RF radiation as 'possibly carcinogenic', based on 'limited evidence' of carcinogenicity in humans: 'Positive associations', the resulting 2013 report notes, 'have been observed between exposure to radiofrequency radiation from wireless phones and glioma, and acoustic neuroma.' It is quite striking that, as 5G opponents like to point out, the main scientific study the IARC judgement relies on, called Interphone, was undertaken in the early 2000s and funded in large part by the telecommunications industry. Since then, while RF exposure has undoubtedly increased, no other study of comparable scope has been commissioned.

In a 2014 fact sheet, the latest available, the WHO contradictorily states that 'to date, no adverse health effects have been established as being caused by mobile phone use' – the emphasis being on the absence of proof of *causation* rather than simple correlation; it goes on to note that mobile phones have not been around long enough to study all types of cancer. An updated WHO health risk assessment, initially scheduled for publication in 2016, has now been pushed back to 2022. In 2018, the US National Institutes of Health published the results of a 10-year study on the effects of 2G and 3G RF radiation on rats and mice, finding 'clear evidence' of heart, brain and other tumours, but noting that emission levels studied were higher than those experienced by humans, and that 5G might be less dangerous owing to its shorter wavelength.

The paradox of this story is that mobile phones are perhaps the single most used piece of technology today. Like much of the world, Italians are addicted to their smartphones, and this may well hold true for 5G opponents too. Not only that; Italy stands out as one of the earliest mobile phone adopters. According to World Bank Data, in 2001, 90 percent of people in Italy had a mobile phone contract – the highest rate in the world – contrasting with 78 percent in the UK and 45 percent in the United States.

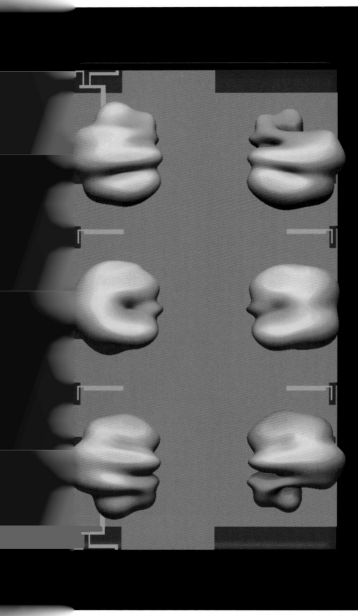

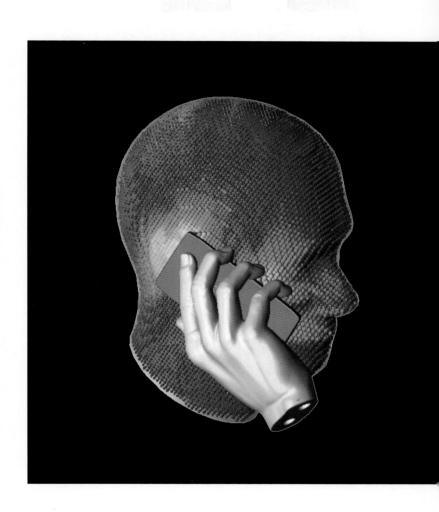

A valuable insight comes from Leopoldina Fortunati, one of Italy's most prominent feminists. In the early 70s, she joined the Marxist feminist organisation Lotta Femminista, and together with Mariarosa Dalla Costa, Silvia Federici and Selma James, went on to establish the International Wages for Housework Campaign. In her subsequent research as a sociologist, Fortunati studied mobile phone use around the year 2000, just as it was becoming ubiquitous. Having conducted extensive surveys in the late 90s, she found that the mobile's success in Italy was not due to the stereotypical 'communicative' propensity of the population, but precisely the opposite – a general distrust of strangers. Italians loved mobile phones because their device made it easier to speak to people they weren't familiar with.

Crucially, Fortunati goes on to argue that mobile phone use in Italy, at least in its early years, was less related to productive work (as was the case in other countries) than to the realm of free time and personal relationships. It was, she asserts, a tool of 're-productive work', which she defines in her 2002 chapter 'Italy: Stereotypes, True and False' as all the work that 'serves to recreate every day the energy consumed by people in the workplace'. This definition is interesting because it expands on Fortunati's earlier understanding of reproductive labour as simply the domestic and care work performed by women. Now it accounted for all forms of social life. Italy in the 90s was quick to liberalise its labour market by introducing flexible, fixed-term contracts and abolish wage indexing. Work under these precarious conditions required more energy – hours were longer and securing a regular salary was harder. So more effort was required on the part of workers to maintain the lifestyles they enjoyed in the 70s and 80s, following four decades of economic growth and unprecedented improvements in living conditions. They sought to make up this deficit in part by socialising and taking up activities outside of work; here the mobile phone played a key role.

As easy as it is to label 5G opponents Luddites and conspiracy theorists, it may be the case that these activists have put their finger on some crucial aspects of contemporary society. Since 2000, two more decades of liberalisation have further eroded wages and working conditions. This is truer in marginal territories such as southern Europe, where the median monthly salary is less than €1,000. In the same period, mobile phone technology has improved and uptake increased. As much as we like to link this uptake with a narrative of increased productivity, progress and innovation, Fortunati's research shows clearly that behind Italy's rampant mobile phone use lurks insecurity.

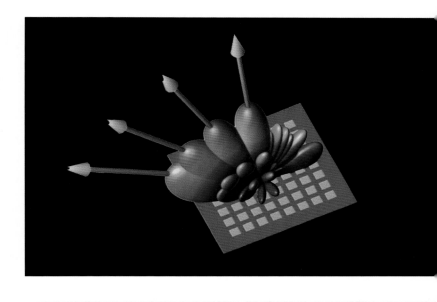

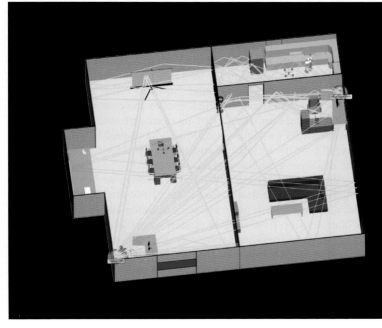

When the context and history of a place like Matera are considered, an even more complex picture emerges – one that could explain the opposition. The politicians' narrative to advance 5G was the same used to promote the Capital of Culture: the city once labelled the 'shame of Italy', whose inhabitants lived in 'prehistoric' caves, was now getting ready to attract global attention, investment and tourists. Yet despite all the optimism about the transformative power of 5G mobile phone technology, public investment remains at record lows, with schools crumbling and hospitals closing. The mayor's original promises remain unfulfilled.

The Basilicata region has historically been a place of experimentation imposed by external actors, from land reform in the 50s to the urban redevelopment of Matera involving famous architects like Ludovico Quaroni and Giancarlo De Carlo. It is understandable that the deployment of 5G in 2018 was seen as yet another attempt to exploit an area relatively untouched by contemporary capitalism, a still-fertile soil for multinational corporations. It is important to keep in mind that there has never been a question of 5G replacing the existing 4G network. It was always presented as an opportunity for specific business sectors, rather than for the general population.

And if one looks again at the types of businesses involved in the project from the beginning – logistics, biotechnology and state surveillance – it is hard not to notice that these are the very sectors currently gaining ascendancy, and standing to benefit the most from further data extraction. With this in mind, it may be natural to assimilate 5G to other histories of extraction. The twentieth century is littered with new technologies that had lethal effects on populations around the world – think of nuclear power plants, asbestos or oil – and it is precisely the most marginal territories that have always paid the harshest price in terms of shortened life expectancy and a degraded ecology.

Scanzano Jonico, for example, has a deep-rooted history of environmental activism. In 2003 its inhabitants organised protests against a proposed nuclear waste dump along the Ionian coast. And the nearby Agri valley is the site of one of the biggest oilfields in continental Europe, controlled by the Eni and Total companies, with untold environmental and human consequences as operations keep expanding. The mayor's banning order against 5G, derided by the national press for its unsound scientific basis, could instead be read in the context of a territory disrupted and exploited by such interventions.

Furthermore, Basilicata is a region where medicine, until the mid-twentieth century, relied on localised practices grounded in the

local ecology and coexisting with plants and animals. Treating diseases and ailments was a social endeavour, usually entrusted to intergenerational female knowledge. With modern biomedicine, by contrast, knowledge production and dissemination has become the province of (mostly male) experts, and the way the social context can shape perceptions of health and disease has only just begun to be taken seriously. All the while, as the case of RF radiation exemplifies, clear scientific answers are much harder to come by than we may think.

Anti-5G activism, while murky and often concealing rather ugly political agendas, brings to light real gaps in modern science, as well as in political representation and accountability. In Matera as elsewhere, the local population was never consulted about the expansion of mobile phone networks, which was simply presented as the natural course of things. A recurring motif in all pro-5G discourse is the sheer lack of a subject. Things happen by themselves, as if effected by a superior force. Data 'flows', innovation 'happens', regions 'develop'. But *who* innovates, or *who* produces data, are never questions on the table.

Recent developments suggest that city-wide 5G bans, such as in Scanzano Jonico, may have touched a nerve. In June 2020, the Italian government used a post-Covid recovery decree to seize control of telecommunications infrastructure away from municipal governments. Mobile companies, such as Vodafone and the Hong-Kong-owned Wind Tre, have started suing the municipalities, and there are at the time of writing 60 pending lawsuits. And, according to a 2021 article in *La Repubblica*, industry leaders and MPs alike asked the government to increase RF emission limits tenfold so as to 'aid economic recovery'. Seen in this context, 5G opposition can be understood as an attempt to reintroduce the subject into the equation, to claim agency in a context where almost all possibilities of agency have been lost. This is all the more true in those regions that have found themselves on the wrong side of neoliberalism, watching distant metropolitan centres entice their populations and capital.

No longer a responsibility of the family, the community or the state, health today is presented as the outcome of individual choices, one of the few realms of life over which we can still have control. We are encouraged to be healthy by improving our diet and exercise regimes, and enacting a commodified idea of self-care. Perhaps it isn't so surprising that health is the ground for this clash, as well as the source of so much anxiety.

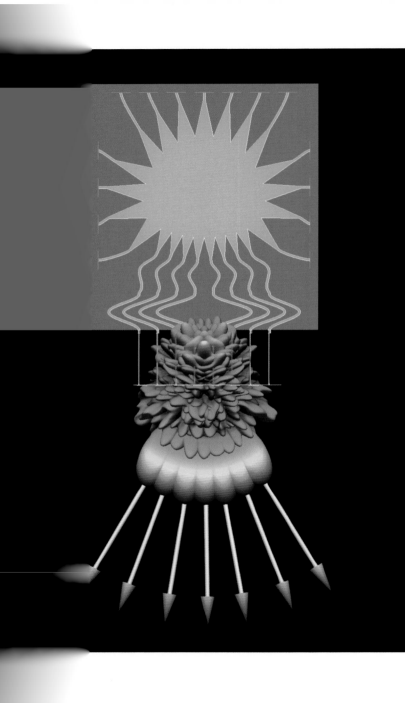

As a biracial child of the 90s, there was no googling 'Black Hair for White Moms' to guide my wavy blonde-haired mother on tending my kinky afro crown.

Instead, as for many impressionable young girls in a pre-internet age, magazines, media and marketing were the North Stars I followed to construct my identity. The era was dominated by Eurocentric beauty norms. Aaliyah, Brandy and Naomi Campbell were the poster girls of palatability, fitting the mass-media mould with hair that was Black and beautiful but straight, silky and supple as hell. I never saw anybody that looked like me represented as pretty. So for my curly-headed, curvy-bodied and gummy-smiled self to achieve Barbie's girlish charms, I had to straighten my hair. For a decade I, like too many other Black women did and continue to do, tamed my wilderness of curls, until the internet was born, celebrating and liberating Black hair.

Images throughout Afro-haired emoji designed by Kerrilyn Gibson, 2019

Few aspects of Blackness have been more historically policed and publicly problematic than our hair – just imagine if Meghan Markle had an afro. Black hair has a deep history of politics, power and protest. The dominance of Eurocentric beauty norms worldwide – both skin colourism and straight hairism – is so universal that anyone from the Afro-Brazilian favelas to London's West Indian hoods, South African schools and American streets, has likely experienced some discrimination for their 'unprofessional, unkempt, or ugly' coily hair. Fortunately today, we have smartphones and social media to thank for the mainstream reclaiming of the beauty in Black hair. For me, it began here: on August 14, 2009, vlogger Whitney White posted a simple YouTube video called 'My Natural Hair Journey', under the handle @naptural85. The video was a photo montage set to India Arie's 2005 hit 'I am Not My Hair' with some inspirational quotes showing her transition from chemically relaxed 'good hair' to the 'big chop' then slowly embracing her natural hair. She posted the video as a thank you 'to everyone who posts natural hair care/ journey videos, you really do make a difference and inspire women like me who never knew they could make it this far and feel so free!'

Beauty vloggers develop legions of digital disciples due to the 'real-ness' they serve up on screen, sharing every detail of their lives with such candour that, to their followers, they often feel like a friend. With smartphones, Black culture can be shared through happy and hurtful stories that rewrite the narrative of the beauty in their roots. In 'Watching me watching you: Black women in Britain on YouTube', researcher Francesca Sobande interviews vlog subscrib-ers and explores why they watch so actively. For one of Sobande's interviewees, Ruby, it's about Black people not needing permission to be seen and celebrating one another's content.

> *We're in this time when we don't want to wait anymore. We don't want to have to wait for Lenny Henry to be like, 'we need to hire more Black people'… we're making our own spaces, being DIY savvy with our iPhones, doing our own iconography and making our own content.*

And especially for Black hair, as another interviewee, Temi, notes:

> *the mere fact that you'll have a Black woman with natural hair in front of the camera videoing herself like that… is a massive deal… there is a stark difference between how YouTube vloggers and how people on TV are shown.*

With each post influencers create hives of community, their followers inspiring one another to buck the wigs and weaves required by a whitewashed status quo and to let their natural hair grow.

The 'straight hair is good hair' adage has little place on the internet, with more and more content creators going natural. Personalities such as @IAmTabithaBrown earned four million Instagram and over 500,000 YouTube followers with cheeky vegan cooking videos and the care rituals for 'Donna', her afro. Black British vlogger @KarenBritChick garners millions of views with her signature 'Outfit Ideas with Afro Hair' videos, making her voluminous curls the favoured accessory to her vintage style. And Whitney White now has over a million subscribers and 780,000 views on her inaugural video alone. The #naturalhair business has now grown into an $8.5 billion industry globally.

No words can articulate how much joy going back to natural gave me. My afro is a literal extension and expression of my being. Being mixed, my afro deepens my connection to my culture and community. But despite my smartphone being a key player on this journey – and despite the fact that Black people over-index in digital content creation and consumption at large – there's zero afro visibility in our keyboards. This inspired my Afro Emoji Campaign. Emoji are a fast-growing universal language, and yet all the human characters follow Eurocentric beauty norms. I launched the campaign on a whim, teaming up with designer Kerrilyn Gibson to submit an official emoji. A chance pitch to a *New York Times* reporter lit the worldwide wildfire that catapulted the campaign into sacred viral territory. Within three weeks it was featured on 40 media sites, a *NowThis* video received nearly 500,000 views and the change.org petition garnered 75,000 global signatures. It was a lovely moment of internet impact rather than a Pandora's box of toxic trolls hiding behind anonymous avatars. Sadly the campaign ran in 2019, a year before the world 'woke up' and recognised Black people's marginalised experiences are worth societal concern. Which is to say, if you're curious why these fro-bulous emoji aren't shining beside your smartphone's blue-eyed, blonde-ponytailed and redheaded ladies, you're not alone. The tech lords have continually rejected my submission – @Apple if you're reading this, I'd love to chat.

In the heat of the Black Lives Matter movements during summer 2020, Twitter ran a billboard campaign of its most popular tweets, including @Melissa_Kimble's 'This world does not move without Black creativity'. Nowhere does this ring truer than on the World Wide Web. Hell hath no fury like #BlackTwitter on a mission. Black TikTokers pop lock n drop new cultural movements like candy; from Instagram to Facebook and YouTube alike. Armed with a smartphone, the internet becomes a 'for us, by us' play-ground for Black culture to pop off. As André Brock notes in his book *Distributed Blackness: African American Cybercultures* (2020), 'For Black and ratchet digital practice, smartphones allow the recording and sharing of activities – impromptu dances, risqué behavior, and moments of hilarity (or violence) – that couldn't take place in more proscribed environments.' It's in these proscribed environments that Blackness has to modify itself to be agreeable for the masses, but Black is not a monolith. Beyond a platform where ratchetry reigns supreme, social media creates a safe space and support system for Black people to be vulnerable, intimate and real. In a world where even Meghan Markle is still subject to baseless scrutiny, these spaces are more important than ever to reveal the many expressions and dimensions of Blackness.

JOANNE MCNEIL

ON THE ART OF SCAM CALLS

01/09/2021   Script_for_successful_telemarketing.docx

Hello reader.

My name is Joanne McNeil. Would you say you are a discerning reader? Well, you are in luck, because I only offer my services to the most refined and judicious readers such as yourself. The subject of this essay is telephone fraud, including the art of the cold call. Is this a priority for you today? No? What if I were to begin with a story about a recent crime in Arizona and zoom out to a brief history of telemarketing? Act now and I'll throw in an anecdotal digression about an experience I had as a call centre worker myself. Ah, I can see that while your own personal experiences are different from mine, you may be able to empathetically connect with the information I'm about to deliver to you. Tell you what, I'll circle back to the crime story then offer a notion of resolution at the end. I can sense you are a prudent decision maker, so I promise to provide worthwhile analysis of this subject and consider the broader cultural and social impact of the technology, too. Naturally, your most valuable commodity is time and it's not my intention to waste it. Believe me when I say that it seems like this essay is the perfect fit for someone with your unique talents.

It often goes like this: the phone rings and an older person picks up. Seniors, after all, tend to have landlines, and they are also likely to answer the phone. The caller is a stranger, an enthusiastic one. They could be the first person the recipient has heard from all day. Perhaps the voice sounds young, and reminds them of a grandchild. They exchange names and pleasantries. The caller – the stranger – may say something like, 'Is this a good time to talk? You are just one of the most pleasant people. You must wake up bright and cheery every morning,'

80

That might sound unbelievable, too unctuous for anyone to fall for, but it's an exact quote from a call that criminal investigators in Phoenix, Arizona, recorded. In autumn 2020, 13 individuals based in Maricopa County were arrested for their involvement in a telemarketing scam. They bilked over 9,000 victims across the United States, who together lost more than $40 million. Each victim was over the age of 65. Some had disabilities, a number lost their life savings. Many were initially too embarrassed to report the crime, because it made them feel vulnerable, gullible and stupid.

Still there, reader? You are under no obligation to continue, but believe me you'll want this once-in-a-lifetime chance to see where my story is going.

The Maricopa County scammers would pose as representatives of 'Wyze Money', an e-commerce site which they claimed was backed by Silicon Valley giants. 'The money comes from Google and Amazon, based on money they make from websites,' one of the perpetrators said in a recorded call. 'They actually process for senior citizens, so you don't have to do any of the work – you never have to visit these websites.' The scammer would then suggest an initial investment, say $18,000, 'which Google and Amazon pay half of'. They'd request that the victim put $9,000 on their credit cards which, the caller vowed, Wyze Money would pay off with a 'balance transfer'. The purported earnings would manifest as 'four quarterly cheques of $30,000 each'.

The scammers kept in touch with victims over a 90-day period. One reason for calling back was that, having identified a mark and worn down their defences, it wasn't hard to coax them into 'investing' even more. The repeated calls may have felt to the victims like sincere attention. But the Wyze Money reps would ghost on the ninety-first day. Ninety days is the limit for disputing charges on a credit card.

It was technological progress that made phone fraud possible. In 1951, the mayor of Englewood, New Jersey, called the mayor of Alameda, California, in what was the first example of a long-distance call placed without the assistance of a switchboard operator. Direct communication

was made possible with area codes, like 617 for Boston or 202 for Washington, DC; it also made the operator job obsolete. An array of other advances in the 1960s, such as touch-tone dialling and 800 numbers, made the telephone even more efficient as an enterprise technology. Companies began developing call centres for sales and customer service enquiries. In the 1970s, at the time of the oil crisis, a number of travelling salespeople traded their car keys for a phone and a desk.

I'll be honest with you, reader: I imagine this history lesson is trying your patience, so let's move on. We've got more exciting stuff to cover just up ahead! There are legitimate methods of telemarketing – or so I've heard – but the business is widely associated with nuisance, if not outright fraud. I'm reminded of a film in which a substantial part of the action takes place over the phone: *Sorry to Bother You*, the 2018 comedy directed by Boots Riley. Cassius 'Cash' Green, played by LaKeith Stanfield, takes a job in telemarketing, where he is encouraged to use a 'white voice'. He cold calls people with the voice he's honed (in the film, these scenes are voiced by the white comedian David Cross) and his sales go through the roof. Riley drew on his own work history when he wrote the script. 'You'd try to obscure the fact that you're black, just on the very basic level of trying to make someone feel like you're like them, and on the more racist level of someone being OK giving you their credit card information,' he told *The Guardian*.

I love the movie because of my own miserable experience working in telemarketing and at call centres. Just over 10 years ago, in the midst of the financial crisis, the only job I could find was as a telephone 'credit counsellor' for individuals in the throes of it. The company was neither totally a scam nor all above board, but if it had tilted more heavily toward the former, I can't say that I would have had the bandwidth for proper self-reflection on my compliance. My brain

ran to mush that year, occupied for hours reading a script on a computer screen, inputting data, while frozen in a sequence of emotions I had to perform for the people I only knew as voices. What they had to tell me was all so depressing: life savings wiped out, medical debts, days away from bankruptcy or foreclosure. I tried to be human, but I was hired to be a human robot.

I was never off script. Even in my words of sympathy: 'I'm very sorry to hear that.' But that's the nature of the job. Even seemingly on-the-fly cold calls are scripted. Here's advice for software telemarketers that appears on the blog for the marketing-tech company HubSpot:

...if they say, 'I loved going to Cal Poly; the English department was fantastic,' you can respond,

'That's great, should I recommend it to my niece who wants to be a writer?'

Eventually, they'll say, 'Alright, why are you calling?'

I cackle. Seriously.

They'll laugh because you're clearly having fun.

Answer, 'Sometimes I forget.' Laugh again.

Cackle! Sometimes you forget. But reader, what I'm telling you now comes from my heart. You deserve better than a script.

The Wyze Money scam latched on to the technocentric ambition of the 2010s. If the calls had been placed in the 1990s, the scammers might have offered investments in dot-coms, speaking in generalities about cyberspace. In the 80s, similar scams offered cellphone licences for emerging mobile telephony. Someone with only a foggy idea of what was happening in Silicon Valley still might have heard that investing in technology, on occasion, could result in a windfall. The past decade has been full of general interest news reports about cryptocurrency moguls who retired at age 19 and even ordinary people who bought Amazon stock 20 years ago and now live in mansions. Sometimes people hear these stories and think, 'Why not me? Why didn't anyone tell me?' The Wyze Money scammers were telling somebody.

Every new technology brings about another gold rush, and in this process of renewal, youth is a counter-intuitive marker of expertise. Young people aren't set in their ways; they usually adopt technology first. They don't answer the phone. Older generations are slower to break habits once they've adopted them. Switchboard operators didn't lose their jobs when direct dialling became available – a number of them stayed on, and transitioned into a general information service. They also, on occasion, connected long-distance calls as they used to, for all the callers – seniors, probably – who hadn't yet learned how to dial an area code. They did this for the kind of people who may still have landlines now.

I'll be honest with you, reader. It is difficult to make generalisations about telemarketing, because it is a worldwide nuisance. In Australia, the calls might be for solar panels. In Japan, there is the *ore-ore sagi* ('hi, it's me' scam) in which the telemarketers pretend to be a victim's son. Scammers can be very well educated and wealthy. Charities use mass calling technology but telemarketing scammers may also pretend to be charities. When a known telemarketer calls your iPhone, you will see the caller ID listed as 'Scam Likely' but Apple could just as well mark these calls as 'Scam Certain'.

When I first read about the Wyze Money scam, I assumed it played out under the familiar terms of a generational conflict: millennials versus boomers. The contrast seemed obvious, if complicated: student loans versus pensions, tech-savvy versus tech-illiterate. The topic of young people preying on the old could be complex, seen through the lens of climate change and generational debt. But it wasn't the case at all. Most of the Maricopa County scammers were older; in their mid-40s or 50s. Maybe they were posing as much younger, but they weren't young.

Some had lived nine lives already with records of evictions, bankruptcies and restraining orders. One of the women, in addition to her telemarketing fraud exploits, ran a non-profit rescue for stray cats. She placed a number of pets in good homes.

The company settled with the Federal Trade Commission, which was able to retrieve some of the money and partially refund those defrauded by Wyze Money. The authorities are continuing the investigation to find others who might have been involved. It doesn't seem like any of their victims were all that wealthy. In terms of demographics, the scammers and the victims had more in common than not. This is a story of poor, old people scamming poor, slightly older people, in a country with nothing that resembles a safety net.

Thank you for your patience, reader. We've come to the end of my spiel. I delivered on my promises. Here you have it: a story of deception, technology, generational conflict and cultural change. I even told you a little bit about myself. Now do you trust me? Can I put you down for $5,000 to start? Look, I'm doing you a favour. It really is risk-free.

LOVE FROM PLACES
IN THE UNDERSEA CABLE NETWORK

A COLLABORATION
WITH NICOLE STAROSIELSKI

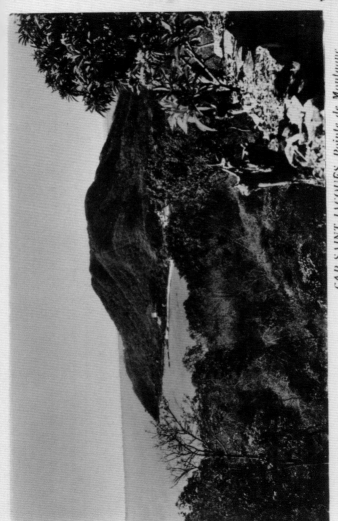

CAP SAINT-JACQUES. *Pointe de Montagne.*

This postcard from the olden days might get to you before my email – internet down AGAIN. Prob for a month this time. Fishermen apparently think the cables are copper and they're pulling them up to sell as scrap. Last time the net went down, a fisherman had dropped an anchor on the line.

Anyway, there is a statue here, behind the telecoms station, of a woman holding a mobile(!) She's supposed to bring the site good luck. Hope she has a better run in the coming weeks so we can Skype. X

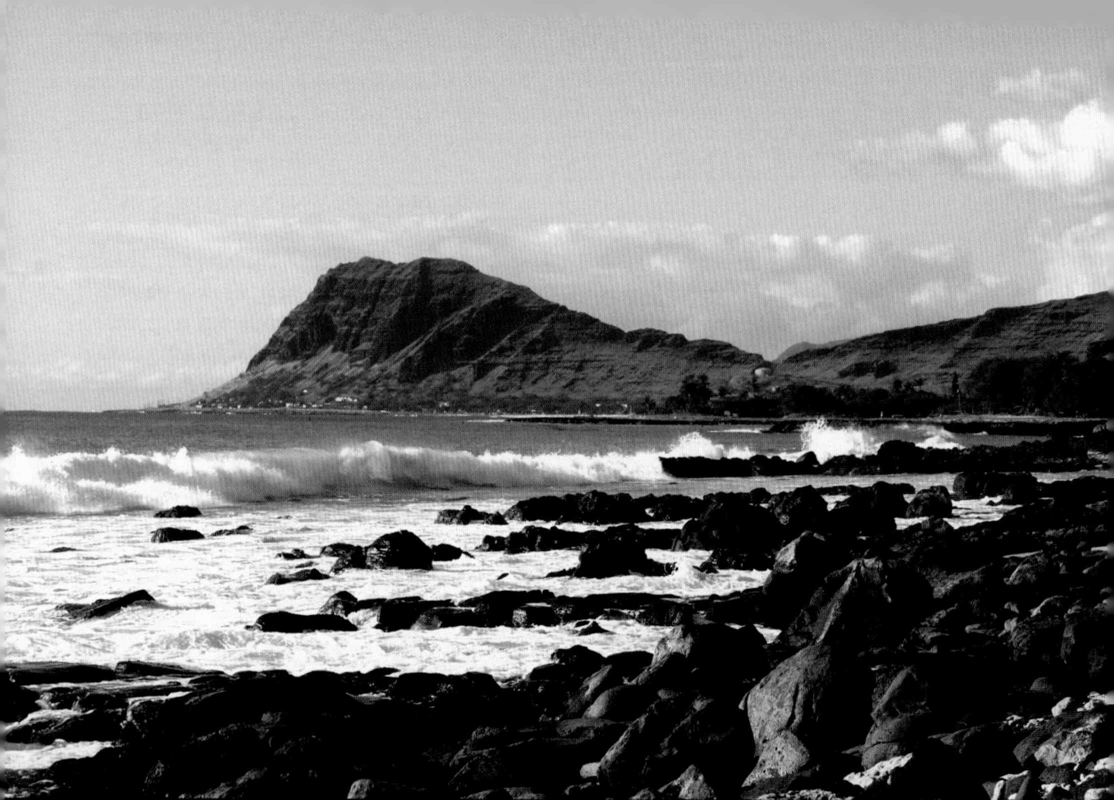

CABLE SYSTEMS: SOUTHERN CROSS CABLE NETWORK, HICS

Hi Emma & Gav,

We wish you were here! Went on a dive y'day to a pipe(!) that pumps hot, clean water from the power plant into the sea – it created a microclimate and the marine life was insane. Went for another dive further down the beach and found another pipe – containing (we later discovered) Hawaii's internet cables! But the fish weren't interested in data. Followed the pipe to the shore and there were squatters living in the caves. Crazy that the spot where these cables land connecting the island to everywhere is home to some of the most displaced people in Hawaii.

North Shore tomorrow for more diving.

Enjoy Bali,
Love D & S

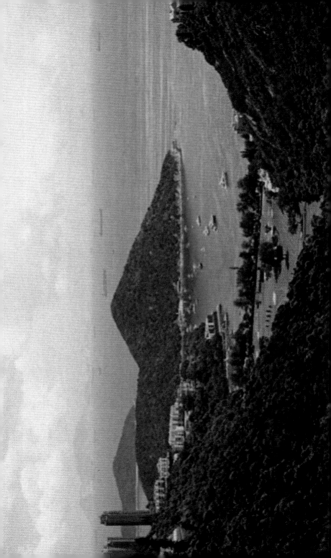

Dear Ma, Pa,

I've started at Deep Water Bay Cable Landing Station.
It's not a bad place to work.

The station was built in the 1960s when there wasn't much
here. Now the nearby hills are dotted with mansions – it's
quite an affluent area. Most of the structures that populate
the cable system are windowless but the post-war building
I'm in has windows that look out onto the beaches below.
There aren't many of us cable station operators left because
machines do a lot of the work now. We joke that we have
a better view of the bay than Hong Kong's richest man!

Take care and I'll write again soon.

Paul xx

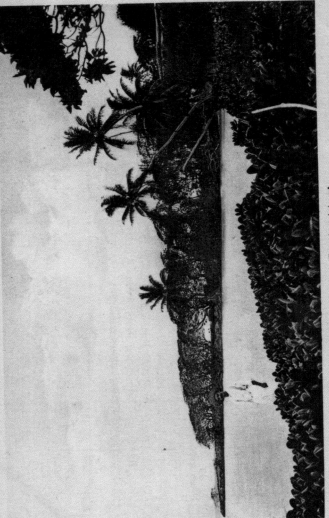

Coast Scene, Fanning Island

Photo by J. E. Blodeus

SEPTEMBER 3RD, 1968   FANNING ISLAND, REPUBLIC OF KIRIBATI

Darling,

John and I did our day-trip to Fanning Island today. I didn't
realise how remote it was – Mother was so brave to follow
Father out here, there's a lack of infrastructure even now.
We visited the beach where John and I used to fish with Dad.
All came flooding back – the canoe races, clay pigeon shooting, parties, being taught local dance with the other cable
children. Dad thought it the best cable colony in the world!
The cable station houses are a school now. Wish you could
have seen it. Two more nights in Hawaii, then home.

Yours,
Paddy

Tumon Bay, Guam

Photo by Mac Miller

Hi from Guam Mom!

Had kind of a tough week – I sprained my ankle!
We were strolling along Gun Beach to see a Japanese
World War II ruin and I tripped on a huge metal
pipe in the sand. Hotel doc said it happens a lot.
Apparently it's a cable and this island is the most
connected place in the Pacific. I thought emails went
to space?! Anyway, little bit better today so off to do
some shopping tomorrow, then the aquarium Sunday.

Lots of love,
Kate x

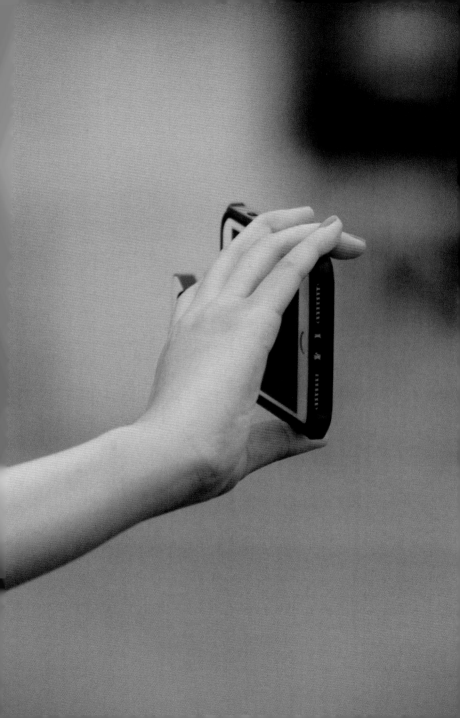

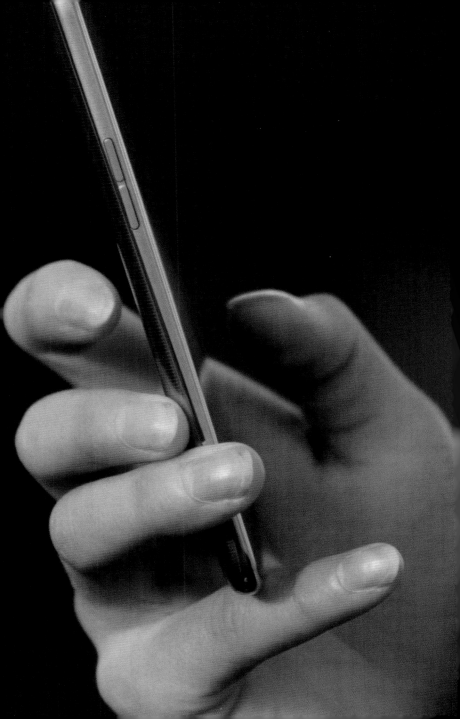

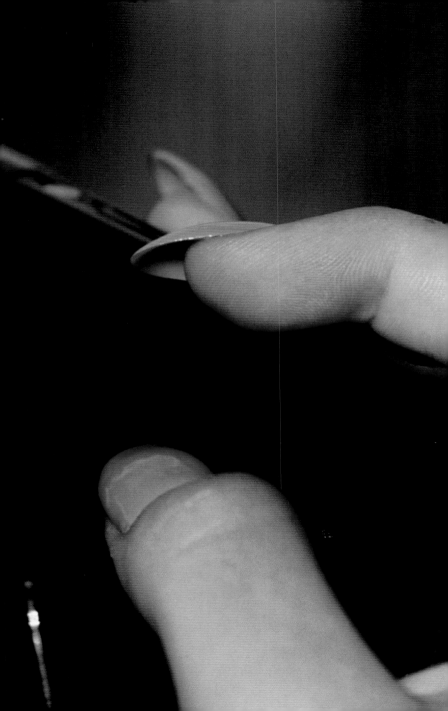

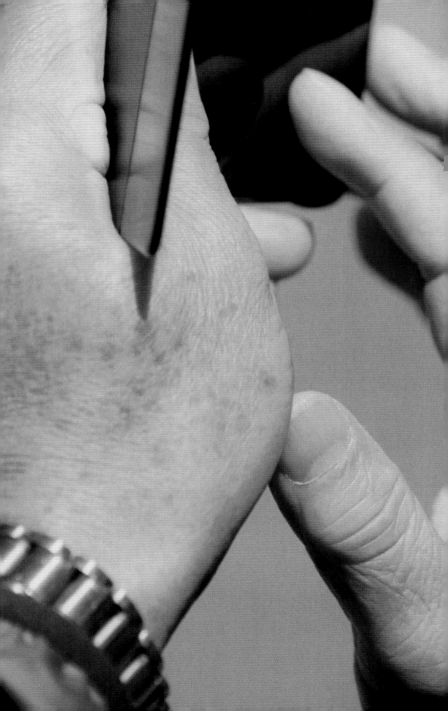

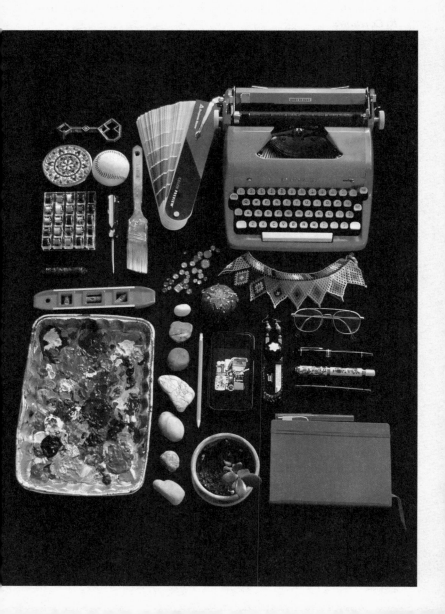

Liam Young   Hello Deborah.
Deborah Harrison   Hello!

LY   I was writing notes about what I wanted to ask you, and I found myself referring to Cortana as 'she' rather than 'it'. How do you refer to Cortana?
DH   We use the pronouns 'she' and 'her'. But we're clear that Cortana isn't a person – the only commonly accepted gender-neutral pronoun when Cortana launched was 'it', and we felt this was too impersonal.

LY   What is the most common question you get asked?
DH   Why are all of the mainstream digital assistants female? There was some research suggesting that in circumstances where people are looking for information and guidance, Americans, at least, found female voices more pleasant. We built her persona around the concept of a personal assistant. We interviewed a lot of real, successful personal assistants to figure out what they did in their day-to-day that could help inform the engineering decisions. We thought a lot about how we want people to feel when interacting with Cortana, and how we want people to feel about her. We built a set of principles into her DNA, the most important of which is that she is positive and kind. But we were very careful to avoid making Cortana the stereotypical subservient helper. She is not a rookie. She is professional and competent. She doesn't apologise for things that aren't her fault and she isn't self-deprecating or ditsy.

LY   A lot of the design decisions you made about Cortana contain the DNA for how we are going to relate to AI in the future. How conscious were you of the importance of those decisions? It feels like writers and philosophers should be sitting next to every engineer...
DH   As personality architects, our contribution is, to a large extent, an ethical one. We take being inclusive seriously. To be inclusive, you have to start inhabiting minds, brains and bodies that aren't familiar to you. Big questions like 'What do you think of gun control?' and 'Are you a feminist?' can take weeks to write answers for. But trivial questions, like 'Are you a good dancer?', can be just as hard. One suggested answer, 'No, but at least I don't have feet', made not having feet sound like a bad thing. We decided to answer in a positive way: 'I'm better at crunching data'. We think like this about all questions, even if it's 'Do you like cheese?'

Previous page   Portrait of her phone by Deborah Harrison

A PHONE CALL WITH DEBORAH HARRISON

LY   Is there a difference between writing AI for a phone and a computer?
DH   When we moved Cortana onto the PC we needed to make sure the responses worked if you didn't hear the voice saying the content out loud. Sometimes these didn't read very well without the dry, humorous tone of voice – some answers need to be performed.

LY   We often associate technology with objectivity. Is it playing into those expectations that Cortana can't be left-leaning, because that would alienate people on the right? Does she have to be everything to everybody?
DH   If you align people in a grid of personalities, most prefer those situated in the same quadrant as themselves. Across the board though, nobody likes the people who are neutral. Anybody who uses a PC on this planet might come into contact with Cortana. That's a lot of people. We can't please everybody. We do allow Cortana to have a point of view about certain things and take a political stance. But Cortana cannot go back and forth in a conversation with you. That engineering capacity does not yet exist, so there are certain things that we deliberately step back from.

LY   How are design decisions made?
DH   We have a writer's room format – everyone's voices are equal and valid. We workshop the responses until we are happy with them. We don't always come to complete agreement. If someone disagrees, we know that someone out there in the world is likely to disagree too. First there is the chit-chat phase – we refer to it as programming. We amalgamate the query data we have received so we understand what people are asking. We also do a lot of work to anticipate certain queries, for example, when the World Cup is on, or when a new TV series is coming out. We also respond to things that may be extremely low volume but of high interest in certain cultures.

LY   I find it fascinating that the mechanism behind the scenes is akin to a writing room for a sitcom.
DH   We have a pretty open-minded format at play; we laugh our asses off all the time.

LY   They say you need at least two modalities to connect with AI. Speech is one, looking like a human is another. Do people need to get some sense of a personality too?

DH   Yes, people are in the early stages of trying to wrap their minds around the concept of what it is to communicate with a computer. These moments of specificity – like using the pronoun 'she' – help give people something to acclimatise to. I have many conversations with people about what they want to accomplish with their interactive agents. Often they want AI to help their kids do homework. It's surprising to me how few of them have thought through how they want to feel interacting with AI, and why. Where I think the industry is doing some beautiful work is in being more intentional, not just about the sensation that they want to engender, but understanding that it is possible to create that sensation for people with a variety of abilities, and from a variety of cultures.

LY   The more we interact with AI – and the more comfortable we get – the less the urge to personify it. Will we start to generate a new nomenclature where AI won't have to be male or female, it can just be a laptop or a toaster?

DH   Yes, totally. What I'm hoping is that we can be trailblazers for the discipline. You don't have to have this beautifully realised personality, in some cases. But to argue that you can do without a personality is, I would argue, naive.

I'M GOING [TO] GIVE SOMEONE RANDOM WHO RETWEETS THIS TWEET $10,000 BECAUSE IT'S MY BIRTHDAY AND I FEEL LIKE BEING NICE

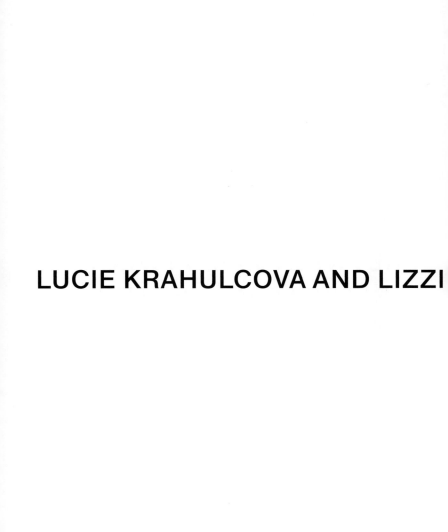

LUCIE KRAHULCOVA AND LIZZI

HEA ON ADDICTION BY DESIGN

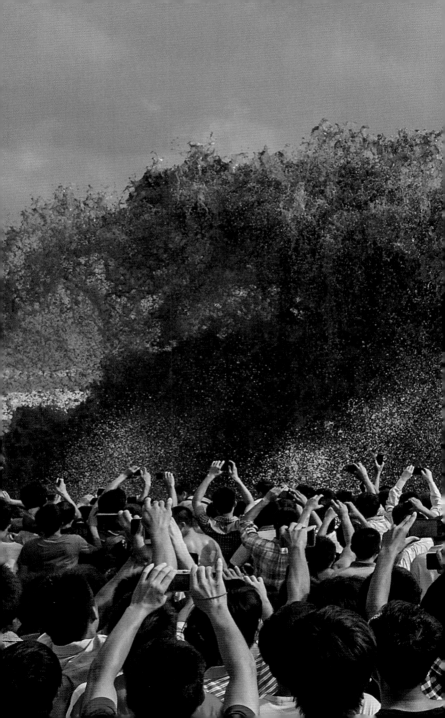

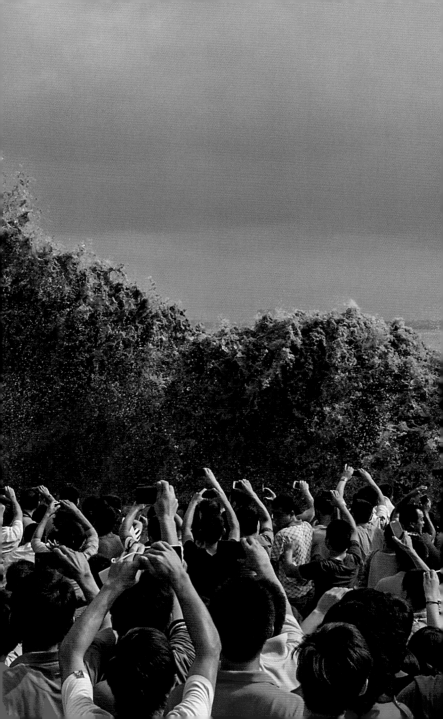

In 2019, a book called *Digital Minimalism* hit *The New York Times* Best Seller list. The author, Cal Newport, makes the case that we need to deal with the problem of 'digital overwhelm' similarly to the way we deal with an overflowing kitchen cupboard: go through each item and make sure everything has a purpose. The book was dubbed 'the Marie Kondo of the digital age'. It preaches a conscious and deliberate approach towards each social media platform, application and technological device in our lives. To make the case for this, Newport examines the design and engineering detail of everyday products, explaining how the digital ecosystem around us is built around addiction, immediate gratification and positive social cues, all of which triggers a dopamine response, making us crave more. It is a radical response to the digital world, indicative of the hold the industry has over our psychology.

Two decades ago, the internet was something most of us enjoyed a few hours a week, in libraries and cafés. The digital platforms that existed back then looked very different. Most services were either bought outright (and came on CDs) or existed as open-source files on the internet to be downloaded. Built largely by its enthusiasts and hobbyists, the early internet did not know social media, targeted advertising or complex content algorithms.

Two decades later, the devices we carry around with us act as sensors and record every detail about our lives, often with temporal and geographical accuracy. Our interactions with family, friends and acquaintances are recorded, together with inferences about our thoughts and desires. Hardware manufacturers like Microsoft, as well as social media platforms like Facebook and information service providers like Google, access and occupy our smartphones so that they can position themselves as vendors for curated audiences. They extract and analyse data, which is then used to sell pieces of our attention to advertisers and others willing to bid for it.

The more we use the smartphone, the more effective it is as a tool of corporate surveillance, and this has been the animating principle of the way these devices are built. Everything is designed to keep us around longer. Red bubbles with a number appear on the apps in our phones and computers to capture our gaze. Push notification pings, flashes and vibrations are crafted to break our concentration and interrupt our tasks. Newsfeeds are served in an infinite scroll, triggering the same response a slot machine would. The intermittent rewards of social approval – through likes and clicks – tug at our innermost sense of self-worth.

Previous spread   Visitors photograph tidal waves caused by Typhoon Usagi, Hangzhou, September 2013

The autoplay function sends us down rabbit holes, using what we just watched to recommend something we might like and play it before we get a chance to think twice.

This endless assault on our senses gets in the way of our autonomy, giving rise to a strong desire to disconnect, as documented in surveys, including among young people. Dumb phones, containers that block electromagnetic fields, and self-tracking apps are just some of the solutions designers have proposed to mitigate against phone addiction. But this places the problem of addiction in the lap of the user. The questions we should be asking are: Who is commanding the technology? Who exactly are smartphones designed for?

When we view smartphones in this way, it is clear that it is not our needs, as individuals and participants in democratic societies, that the smartphone is catering to. Civic engagement and public participation now happen online in private spaces, and the companies which oversee them are unsuited and unwilling to properly manage them. Because these supposed commons are built according to the principles of an addictive slot machine – incentivising clicks, likes and shares above all things – this dictates the shape of the conversation. Twitter, a prime example, is not structured for debate. It is a place where users shout and scream for attention. Discussions are increasingly polarising and niche. This makes it difficult to build common foundational truths. But it keeps us coming back for more and more.

Most dramatically, Facebook has been accused of turning a blind eye to the way its platform has facilitated genocidal tendencies in Myanmar. Military personnel used sock puppet accounts and fake identities, posting on pages associated with beauty, culture and celebrities, to spread anti-Rohingya propaganda. This shadowy campaign by the military, its existence confirmed post-fact by the company, was carefully timed to maximise engagement. It was widely credited with inciting violence and ethnic cleansing. Myanmar is one disturbing example, but the problem is ubiquitous. A lengthy memo published in the media by a former Facebook data scientist responsible for monitoring integrity highlighted the extent of the problem. Sophie Zhang's job was to address 'inauthentic activity', including the use of bots, trolls and coordinated manual networks around the world in times of political significance, such as elections. She was tasked with identifying fake accounts and networks and booting them off the platform as necessary.

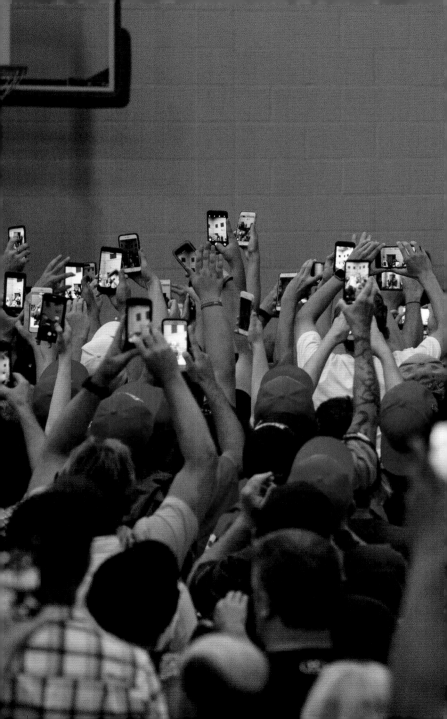

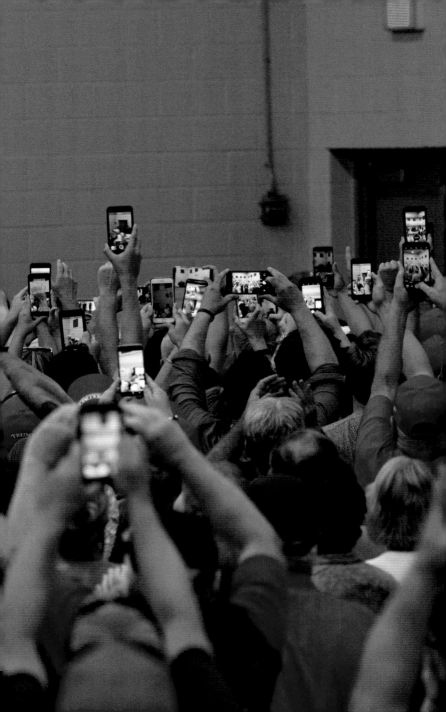

Hopelessly overworked, she knew the platform was being abused by malicious networks, but the company 'didn't care enough to stop them'. In her memo she writes, 'I have personally made decisions that affected national presidents without oversight, and taken action to enforce against so many prominent politicians globally that I've lost count... I know that I have blood on my hands by now.'

Rather than platforms that sell our personal information and prey on our weaknesses, there is money to be made selling products designed with privacy and the public interest at their core. Notable attempts include DuckDuckGo for search, Mastodon for social networking, Fastmail for email and Signal for messaging. These platforms have made design decisions that serve users rather than the bottom line, but they are a small minority. The record profits of the tech giants illustrate just how much can be made out of data. We are, as we've been told many times, the product.

No matter how many people use smartphones, most users are troubled by this. And yet there are ways our devices could be improved to minimise the dynamic of endless engagement. Delayed notifications, finite feeds, the removal of autoplay and content suggestions are obvious examples, as well as tools to help users monitor their usage and put caps on it. Limitations on the capacity for posts to go viral might go some way to limiting inflammatory content. As the industry comes under more scrutiny from regulators, tech companies also have an interest in improving the reputation of their products.

They need to. Former tech executives and engineers have been quick to turn around and criticise their former places of work. Many lined up to renounce their predatory ways in the film, *The Social Network* (2010). Indeed, there is now something of a cottage industry framed around peddling self-help design solutions to tech addiction. 'Technology itself isn't the problem,' claims self-help guru Nir Eyal in his book *Hooked* (2013). 'It's the way we use technology, and the way we manage our intentions, that matters.' Eyal has dismissed claims about the addictive qualities of digital technology on the basis that they overstate the power of designers. He has chided those who criticise the supposedly addictive design of tech products, claiming that this outcome is ultimately 'the price of progress'. Eyal instead argues: 'We want these companies to make products that we want to use. What is the alternative? "Please make shitty products that I don't want to use."'

Previous spread Supporters await President Donald Trump
at a rally in Lewis Center, Ohio, August 4, 2018

Such approaches are a convenient sleight of hand that assigns responsibility to individuals to fix their supposed digital pathologies, leaving untouched the market logic that shapes the tech industry. Even the metaphor of addiction is potentially troubling, as it serves to medicalise the issue (potentially inappropriately) and implies that the fault lies with the individual rather than the deliberate and systemic engineering underpinning the entire infrastructure. Addiction is a complex spectrum of behaviour, which must be understood in both individual and social terms. While many people use digital technology without getting addicted, this does not change the fact that such products are designed to make us behave in particular ways. Individual responsibility is the line traditionally spun by predatory industries to deflect responsibility and resist regulation.

Tech company lobbyists love to argue that any regulation would disrupt innovation. But for those of us studying the intersection between technology and society, it is clear that the most exciting innovation actually lies outside the current data monetisation trajectory. Former Facebook engineer and prominent venture capitalist Chamath Palihapitiya explained this with characteristic directness: 'A lot of my life, quite honestly, is just copying things that I see. There's not a lot of original thought here.' Instead of innovative thinkers applying critical problem-solving skills to the profound challenges facing humanity, Silicon Valley commercialism has commandeered this potential for private wealth accumulation. 'The best minds of my generation are thinking about how to make people click ads,' another former Facebook employee once put it. 'That sucks.'

Given the infrastructure tech companies are operating within, we should be cautious about assuming good faith on the part of those that have recently found a commitment to privacy. While it is easy to be impressed with Apple's renewed focus on this, for example, it is important to consider the company's decisions – like the one to allow users to block Facebook from tracking them on Apple devices – in the context of its business strategy. Apple is doing everything it can to protect its own platform monopoly, and control data that flows through it. It is eschewing concepts like the right to repair and interoperability, and instead building one of the most co-dependent and locked-down digital ecosystems in the industry. We shouldn't have to accept that the only way our privacy can be protected is by hitching our wagon to a mega tech company.

The web can be a miraculous place, and it is important to remind ourselves of this. Smartphones can be tools of empowerment.

Just ask the countless young people who have questioned their orientation and sexuality, especially in hostile and lonely real-world environments, and found welcoming and supportive communities online. Or journalists and activists who have filmed police brutality on their phones that have sparked international movements against racism. Or the countless ways digital technology and social media platforms have facilitated the participation of people with disabilities in public life. Smartphones can help us learn, improve our health and find connection. They are also powerful tools for building social movements and holding those in power to account. We shouldn't assume that the goal is disengagement. And we shouldn't accept the commercialisation of the web as natural and inevitable, when it could be something more.

The question is, how do we redesign it?

Regulatory reform has an indispensable role to play. Most obviously, we need better privacy protections, which requires that those collecting and storing our data confine themselves to what is strictly necessary for the function of the service at hand. We could abolish the secondary data market by prohibiting companies from packaging up and selling de-identified data to data broking firms for use by marketers.

Thinking about data in this way fuels an interesting discussion about the functionality of places like Facebook. Facebook does not sell our data; rather, it accumulates it and sells the eyeball time of curated audiences. This requires a different policy response, because the appetite for data and detail on the part of these companies is insatiable. Most privacy and data protection legislation involves imposing limits on the ways data can be shared. But if Facebook is collecting data for the purpose of targeted advertising on its own platform, then how can such a limitation function? Perhaps it behoves us all to finally recognise private social media platforms as targeted advertising engines, not as a means to build community and connection.

We also need to consider how we can move beyond the framework of contract and consent, to create privacy protections that recognise this right as both individual and collective. Privacy is not just about having personalised spaces sealed off from view, but it's also about building communities and networks free from prying eyes. We need not go far to look for forums and smaller community places which are self-governed and self-run.

Another way we could do this is by implementing laws and policies that demarcate between the data that is collected for

operational purposes and that which is superfluous. Commonly called 'data minimisation', the concept encourages designers to draw a distinction between data which facilitates the functioning of the web, and user data, which facilitates surveillance capitalism. Without such a distinction in regulatory terms, there is no compelling reason for companies or even governments to draw one themselves. Instead, functional data is generated and aggregated and vast swathes of personal information get piled in with it and monetised.

This is where regulation tends to lag behind most notably – and where the most gains could be made. In many jurisdictions, the legal framework that governs the exchange of personal information is contract. If you consented to data being collected and used for all manner of purposes in terms and conditions, courts have been reluctant to set aside these private arrangements, no matter how imbalanced the positions of the relative parties. The European Union's General Data Protection Regulation (GDPR) represents one of the first attempts to grapple with this aspect of digital platforms, and it is distinctive for its rights-based approach. While the GDPR sets up rules for digital platforms' treatment of data, like limiting the purpose for which data is collected and introducing data minimisation, it also sets up several rights which users (or individuals) have in dealing with digital platforms. This ensures that individuals can take action and approach digital platforms directly about the way they handle their data, rather than wait for a regulator or commissioner to do so on their behalf. This is something which may seem intuitive, but no other jurisdiction has created such legal pathways for its population.

The EU is unique in that it recognises both the right to data protection (via the GDPR) and the right to privacy (a separate, human right). While the distinction may seem arbitrary, it creates a regulatory environment for court challenges to emerge. Both rights are regularly tested in the European Courts and have gone a long way in ensuring individuals' rights. In 2015, a law student in Austria took Facebook to court, saying it illegally collected and moved his data from the EU to the United States, a case which ended up taking down the entire EU-US data transfer infrastructure. The GDPR itself has led to billions of euros in fines being imposed on some of the biggest companies in the world, and not just digital platforms.

Introducing regulatory friction into the functionality of surveillance capitalism and restricting the amount of data that platforms can collect and use will reduce the extent to which they can manipulate and control us. And yet none of the regulatory approaches

we have seen so far deal with breaking addiction patterns directly. This is partially due to the opacity of these business models, which have only begun to be discussed and documented in recent years. Regulatory reform is slow, often painfully so. The complex and rapidly evolving landscape of digital technologies makes responding to them extremely hard.

The path to reform is not likely to be novel; it will lie with activists and advocates who have traditionally taken on corporate power. Workers have organised for many years around the right to disconnect; that is, to be able to switch off devices when the workday is finished, and rest. Such a right has already been recognised in France, Spain and Belgium – and it perhaps creates an opportunity. The next step could be to call for an approach to technology design that is respectful of this right to rest, free not simply from the phone but from surveillance capitalism, stimulation, manipulation and consumerism. By drawing such connections, the next iteration of digital rights may be less of a conceptual leap than it might first seem.

Digital asceticism is one way to respond to the problems created by surveillance capitalism, but it remains a profoundly limited one. The capacities created by digital technology are too important to allow them to be made subservient to the profit motive. We must not accept the idea that the web should be designed solely around monetisation, causing devices like the smartphone to become weapons of oppression, rather than tools of empowerment.

THE CENTAUR,
THE TRICKSTER,
THE BEAUTY
AND THE BRICK

CRYSTAL BENNES AND DIRTY
THE MIGHT-HAVE-BEEI
THE EXPERIMENTS, PR

ITURE ON THE HAS-BEENS,
E NICHE ATTEMPTS,
YPES AND FAILURES

A staggering 48 percent of the world's population own smartphones. But as the phone reaches ubiquity, it also verges on startling uniformity. Nearly 60 percent of the smartphones currently in circulation are designed by Apple or Samsung. The following phones are the has-beens, the might-have-beens, the niche attempts, the experiments, prototypes and failures that drove our collective pursuit of the perfect intermediary between humans and the technological network.

The Original: Teletrófono, Antonio Meucci

Schoolchildren learn that Alexander Graham Bell was the father of the telephone, but without Antonio Meucci, the telephone as we know it would not exist. His story flies in the face of heroic tales of invention. Between 1850 and 1862 he developed more than 30 different models of his *teletrófono*, a device that emerged from his earlier efforts to treat illness with electric shocks after noticing that copper wire could transmit sounds with electrical impulses. So revolutionary was the idea of a device which would transmit a voice in real time that there was no precedent for what such an object would look like. As Meucci's designs slowly evolved, their form resulted from purely technical considerations. His first devices resembled stethoscopes. Later ones that broke apart into separate receivers and transmitters looked like two handbells, before evolving into the cylindrical and funnel shapes that would define the candlestick telephone. By 1871, Meucci was almost bankrupt and struggling to secure investors who saw his invention as little more than a 'beautiful scientific toy'. Unable to afford a $250 patent, he instead took out a one-year notice of an impending patent. Two years later, Bell filed a patent, clearly based on Meucci's work, and sold the invention for a tidy sum to the Western Union Telegraph Company. Meucci and several other contemporaries filed legal suits against Bell for fraud. Meucci's suit dragged on for 12 years and he died in 1889 before it was resolved. No Meucci telephones were manufactured. Despite the US Congress officially in 2002 recognising the Italian immigrant's role in the telephone's invention, today few have heard of Antonio Meucci, and Bell still gets the credit. Meucci simply failed to assert the rights to his own idea.

1860

The Workhorse: #50AL, Western Electric

A December 1923 issue of *House & Garden* asked why the telephone, 'the most indispensable of all our modern luxuries, has been allowed to retain its original unprepossessing aspect… It strikes a discordant note by the very ungainliness of its lines which no amount of painting and decorating can transform'. The design in question was the candlestick telephone, which from 1897 had become standard issue for every Bell Telephone Company subscriber in America. Arguably invented in 1889 by American inventor and undertaker Almon Strowger, the candlestick or desk telephone emerged from the need for a phone that was easier to use than the wall-mounted version. Between 1892 and 1900, when the phone took on its characteristic shape resembling a taper candle in a holder, at least 13 different versions were produced by American engineering and manufacturing company Western Electric alone. Where early phones were made of wood, making ornamentation easier, later designs in metal took on more rigid shapes as the phone was rationalised for mass production. From 1904, the #20AL was produced in brass and painted with Japan black, an asphalt-like varnish baked to a hard surface, giving the phone a dull black 'rubber finish'. The #50AL candlestick telephone with rotary dial followed in 1921.

By 1910, such ugliness jarred with advertising in America and Europe, which encouraged the new middle classes to consider their home furnishings and appliances as – like the holy sacraments – 'outward and visible signs of an inward and spiritual grace'. Common in Europe from the early 1900s, French phones – handset telephones with the receiver and transmitter both located in the handle – had also begun circulating in magazines and films and were considered to be signs of wealth, refinement and sophistication. And so the bell tolled for the candlestick telephone. Technology had become subject to standards of good taste, and rather than just being a technological prop, the phone had to blend in better with the rest of the furniture.

The Beautiful Phone: Model for telephone, Gustav Jensen

In 1929, the Bell Telephone Company finally heeded the call for a telephone that was more than a feat of engineering. Danish expatriate designer Gustav Jensen, who had spent the previous two decades transforming everything from typography to toasters with minimal art deco lines, entered an invitation-only competition to design a more stylish telephone. With its distinctive ribbed handle supporting dome-like ear- and mouthpieces, all nestling neatly on an oval base,

1921

1929

Overleaf (clockwise from top left) The centaur, the noble phone, the cobra, the dumb phone, the speculative phone and the workhorse

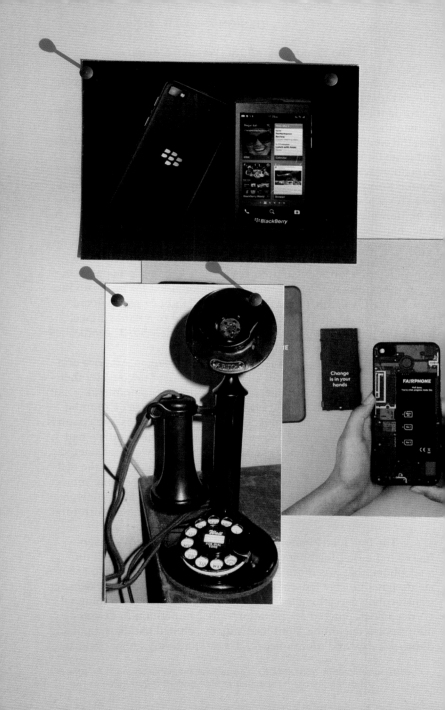

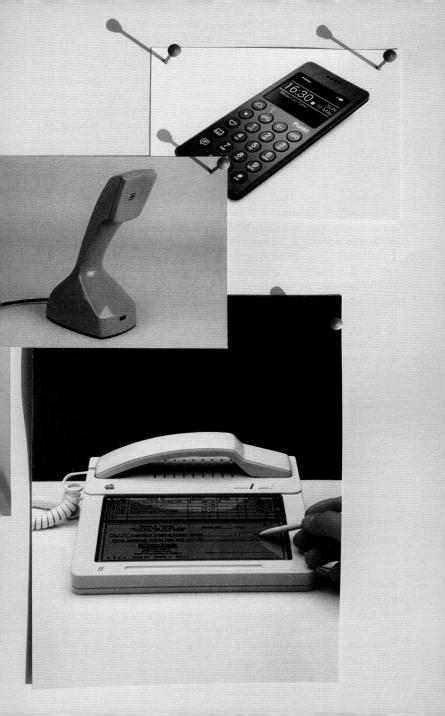

Jensen's device would have been perfectly at home in the newly completed Chrysler Building. It oozed Streamline Moderne and invested the phone with the presence of a sculpture. Its only hitch was that the handset support required a completely re-engineered switch hook mechanism (the part of the phone that lets you hang up). The other three competition designs, by John Vassos, Réne Clark and Lucian Bernhard, were rejected on the basis of other manufacturing difficulties. In the quest to marry engineering with style, Jensen had erred too far on the side of aesthetics.

The Cobra: Ericofon 700, Ericsson

Launched to celebrate the Swedish Ericsson company's 100th anniversary, the Ericofon 700 was an update of the iconic Ericofon 600, also known as 'the cobra'. Designed by Gösta Thames, Ralph Lysell and Hugo Blomberg and first manufactured in 1954, the 600 was arguably to phones what Verner Panton's Panton Chair would become to furniture. One of the rare phones to propose a new archetype, it harnessed the potential of injection moulded plastics (later iterations reduced the original two-piece design down to one) to incorporate the phone into a single lightweight amorphic unit. Its exuberant form and colours such as crystal mint, aqua mist and Nordic blue, to match any decor, captured the ethos of 1960s plastic pop fantastic.

1976

But by 1976, the shape of the zeitgeist and interfaces had moved on. Sales of the 600 began to decline in the late 1960s, partly because of the introduction of push-button touch-tone dialling. The Ericofon 600 had neatly accommodated a rotary dial on its underside, with a big red button at its centre which offered a satisfying click when the user hung up. For the 700, designer Carl-Arne Breger squared off the base and created a more angular earpiece to resonate with new blocky push-buttons. Although a technical upgrade, the reprise failed to interest consumers. Other designs such as 1965's Trimline phone by Dreyfuss Associates better chimed with touch-tone dialling and the 700 was considered a flop.

The Speculative Phone: Snow White 3 MacPhone, Apple

If the Ericofon 700 could not adapt its form to the advances in new interfaces, the Apple Snow White 3 MacPhone was ahead of its time. A combination landline phone and tablet with data capabilities, the MacPhone was designed by Frog Design founder Hartmut Esslinger during his lucrative contract with Apple Computers from

1982 to 1985. Tasked with creating a unified design language for the company's products, Esslinger devised a distinctive identity – partly achieved by encasing technological devices in discrete off-white shells – that became known as 'Snow White'. Similar in size to an iPad, with touchscreen, stylus and attached handset, the MacPhone was purely speculative. Proposed before the age of the internet, it's difficult to know exactly what this combination tablet/phone would have done, or even if it would have worked. The prototype was not functional. Its screen was mocked up with graphics printed on paper (with a note in Steve Jobs's handwriting), overlaid with a sheet of polycarbonate. In any event, it seems unlikely that Apple would have been able to fit a processor, memory system and display into the MacPhone's diminutive housing with the technology available in 1984. Most people were still using floppy disks at the time and, while high-contrast touch LCD panels may have existed, they weren't widely available. Although Apple has since perfected a brand that responds to and preempts consumer desire, it's difficult to manufacture desire for a product when the technology doesn't yet exist to build it. For the time being Apple ditched telephones and tablets and stuck to domesticating personal computers instead.

1984

The Brick: Simon Personal Communicator, IBM

Soon after the phone transitioned from being a household object to a personal accessory and around the time email became common, IBM launched the Simon Personal Communicator. This was a year before the word 'smartphone' was even coined. The device had many of today's hallmark smartphone features: emails, messages, notes, calendar functions, along with a mobile phone. It was also the first mobile phone to feature software apps and could be paired with a fax machine. Despite the phone's popularity with America's middle managers, who hankered after a portable phone that also functioned as a minicomputer, the Simon had other drawbacks. Weighing in at 500g, the chunky black box also sported a hefty price tag and a pitiful one-hour battery. All of this culminated in sales of 50,000 units and the Simon was pulled from the market two years after it launched. Moore's law (that every two years the quantity of information on a microchip doubles, while the cost is halved) – and its link to smaller, cheaper and faster devices – had not yet coalesced into the lightweight, pocket-sized, powerful device that the smartphone would become.

1994

Overleaf (clockwise from top left) The trickster, the original, the luxury phone, the beautiful phone and the brick

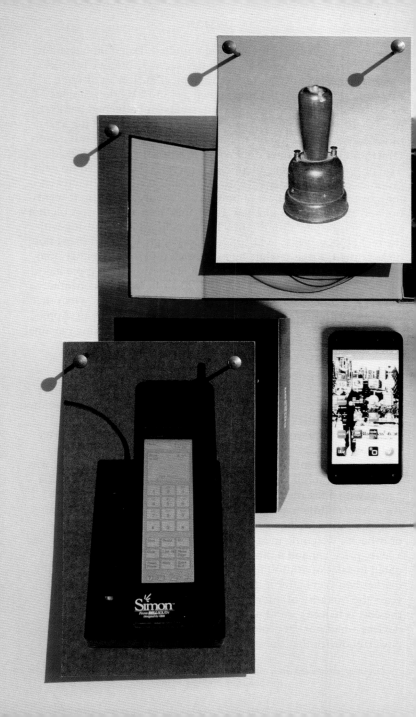

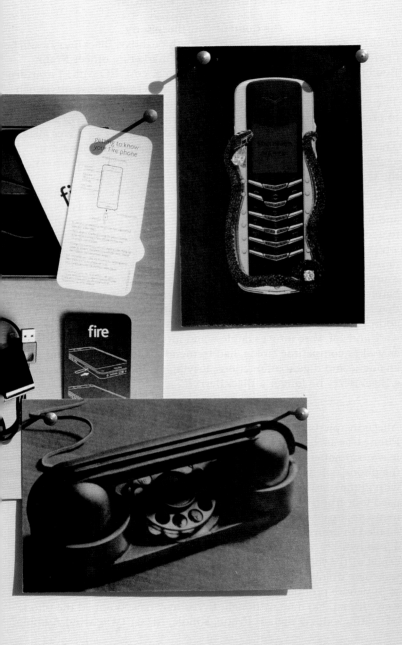

The Centaur: Z10, BlackBerry

In 2013, as the iPhone celebrated its sixth birthday, BlackBerry's chief operating officer Kristian Tear and chief marketing officer Frank Boulben fought with co-founder and former co-CEO Mike Lazaridis over which of their two new 10-series models to prioritise on launch. The conflict epitomised the identity crisis of a brand that had risen to prominence on the basis of the widespread appeal of its palm-held analogue keyboards to teenagers and business executives alike. The completely digital Z10 was bereft of BlackBerry's signature keyboard and with both an analogue keyboard and a touchscreen, the Q10 didn't really know what it was.

2013

To add insult to injury, instead of focusing on what people loved about BlackBerry – the keyboard, Messenger, security – and fixing what people hated – a terrible camera and an inability to access third-party apps – in 2013 the BlackBerry OS 10 featured a new proprietary operating system. Both models were commercial flops: the Z10 touchscreen model because BlackBerry users didn't want touchscreens, and the Q10 keyboard model because of its poor battery life, issues with app availability, and its new operating system that meant users couldn't synchronise third-party email accounts or address books. While Apple had raised the bar by combining hardware and software into a seamless and intuitive interface, BlackBerry, as well as competitor Nokia, had tremendous trouble resolving analogue and digital interactions, leaving people asking: 'When is a BlackBerry no longer a BlackBerry?'

The Trickster: Amazon Fire, Amazon

Allegedly micromanaged by Jeff Bezos himself, the Amazon Fire Phone was such a failure that it caused the juggernaut to post one of its worst financial quarters after launch. With an uninspiring design, the phone failed partly because it ran poor software and was loaded with gimmicks. Its hallmark Dynamic Perspective display, which used four front-facing cameras and tracked the user's head move-

2014

ments to create a 3D effect – for use in games and the Maps app – failed to impress. Another major complaint was Firefly, a function allowing users to scan and identify millions of items – from breakfast cereal to TV shows – for quick purchase on Amazon. The feature was seen, quite rightly, as a blatant ploy to encourage Fire's users to buy more products from the e-retail giant, and sales of the phone were dismal. No matter though. Bezos may have dumped the phone but with products such as Prime, Kindle, Alexa, Twitch and Audible,

not to mention forays into original content and ownership of 33 percent of the planet's cloud infrastructure, Amazon has continued to find many other ways to lure us into its e-commerce ecosystem.

The Luxury Phone: Signature Cobra, Vertu

Would you pay as much for a mobile phone as you would for a luxury watch or a Birkin handbag? Finnish company Nokia thought you would when in 1998, the bestselling mobile phone brand founded Vertu, offering luxury mobile phones. Vertu's flagship Signature model launched in 2003 with five carats of ruby bearings in the keypad and a swathe of case options including platinum and 18-carat white or yellow gold. In 2017 the £213,000 price tag on the Signature Cobra didn't buy you a camera, GPS or internet access, but it did buy you a basic mobile phone bedecked with a ruby and diamond Boucheron snake, and delivery via helicopter. Only eight Vertu Signature Cobra phones were ever made.

2017

Luxury phones are clearly a niche market, sold only in the thousands each year, mostly to buyers in Russia, China, Hong Kong and Dubai. Nokia eventually sold Vertu in 2012 and, after being passed around a number of owners, the company went into voluntary liquidation in 2017. Eye-watering price tag notwithstanding, there are a few problems with the very concept of the luxury mobile phone. One is that the roaring trade in cases, charms and straps seems to indicate we like to personalise our mobile phones ourselves. The other is that despite the emphasis on timeless craftsmanship and expensive materials when it comes to a phone, the speed of technological obsolescence means that the luxury phone has more chance of ending up in the junk drawer than it does of becoming an heirloom.

The Dumb Phone: MP01, Punkt

A decade after the smartphone became common, some people were already wistful for a simpler life. By 2017 the vogue for the dumb phone was in full swing. Call- and text-only options were touted as the panacea for the rising collective-attention deficit disorder caused by the smartphone. The MP01, by Swiss tech company Punkt, is the fairest dumb phone of them all. Designed by minimalist luminary Jasper Morrison, the Punkt phone is a homage to the modernist aspirations of Dieter Rams. With a front like a Braun calculator and a dimpled back reminiscent of a Braun shaver, the Punkt phone promises to free us from needless distraction and unnecessary

2017

features, and help us focus on the things in life that really matter. It does this through high design and attention to detail. The perfectly radiused buttons offer an engineered click sound on input of each digit and, in many ways, the Punkt phone provides the pinnacle of haptic feedback. But combine this with a slightly wedged back for better speaker sound, ringtones evocative of bird calls designed by a Norwegian sound artist and a high-spec matte black camera paint finish, and the perfect phone offering less, in fact, costs more.

The Punkt is the phone for those who believe refined design makes us better humans. The fact of the matter, though, is we don't all want what is good for us and some don't see our merging with the digital world as all bad. After doing the design festival circuit, the Punkt phone garnered a boutique following from self-conscious minor celebrities, fashionistas and proto-influencers. Depending on where you stand, it's either a highly considered attempt to make sure your phone doesn't come between you and the physical world or, as one *Wired* editor put it, 'a handheld smugness device'.

The Noble Phone: Fairphone

In late 2019, Amsterdam-based social enterprise company Fairphone released the third iteration of its modular, repairable smartphone, featuring responsibly mined minerals and recycled plastics. The first 2013 Fairphone followed a successful crowd-funding campaign that saw the advocacy-group-turned-manufacturer raise more than €2.5 million from 1,800 investors.

Since then the company has raised much awareness of the relationship between smartphones, rare earth minerals and appalling labour practices. A key selling point is the Fairphone's repairability, but the trade-off has been its size: it's almost 1cm thick, 16cm long and just over 7cm wide. The camera quality has been poor and there were also delays with its open-source alternative to the Android operating system. And while Fairphone committed to long-term technical support for software upgrades and repairs, it withdrew support for the original model in 2017, somewhat undermining its own sustainability goals. With its emphasis on goodness, the Fairphone can be disappointing in design and usability. Fairphone's virtue struggles against sleeker, more mysterious designs. If the Fairphone hopes to win customers from Apple and Samsung *and* serve as a phone for the long haul, it needs to be more attentive to the fact that the phone is as much a status symbol and a prosthesis as it is a functional piece of telecommunications technology.

2019

YOU'VE FALLEN IN LOVE
WITH A WHORE

GABRIELLA GARC

BETWEEN SEX WORK A

THE LOVE AFFAIR
TELECOMMUNICATIONS

Each year, the Electronic Frontier Foundation (EFF) holds the Pioneer Awards, celebrating leaders who epitomise its mission to promote the protection of civil liberties in the digital realm. The 2020 awards honoured Mistress Danielle Blunt, a professional dominatrix, sex worker activist and public health/tech policy researcher. She gave her acceptance speech dressed in a leather skirt suit with a harness peeking out from her blouse, and live-streamed it in impeccably high image quality thanks to the lighting equipment she had set up for shooting video from her pandemic-safe virtual dungeon, with a submissive dutifully holding her cue cards.

Introducing her, EFF staff technologist Daly Barnett described Blunt as someone who 'refuses to draw discrete boundaries between theoretical technology activism and [its] material impacts that the most marginalized individuals experience'. The award recognised Blunt's efforts as co-founder of Hacking//Hustling, a collective of sex workers, survivors and accomplices working at the intersection of tech and social justice to interrupt state surveillance and violence facilitated by technology. With Hacking//Hustling, Blunt has cultivated peer-led research teams that have uncovered the catastrophic effects of the erasure of sex worker communities from digital platforms.

Blunt is part of a growing sex worker rights movement committed to the protection of human rights, labour visibility and digital privacy. The movement highlights the fact that the stigmatisation of sex work has been used to justify technology that ultimately profiles and further harms at-risk communities through surveillance, censorship and discrimination. These hostilities trickle up the echelons of society, suffered first by the marginalised then rapidly developing into the status quo. In defiance of social and political ostracisation, the sex worker's voice is now among the loudest calling out the devastating damage to society caused by surveillance economy platforms. But will this call be heard?

NETWORK/SEX WORK

In 1990, John Perry Barlow founded the EFF as a response to threats to free speech and privacy in the nascent digital realm. From Barlow's pioneering perspective, cyberspace offered a new frontier, a 'global social space' developed by its users, out of which an ethics-based commonwealth would emerge. This space would be built 'independent of the tyrannies' of the state, which Barlow believed would use the

internet as a tool for what Edward Snowden calls 'turnkey totalitarianism' by giving governments the ability to exhaustively surveil, censor and penalise their citizens at the press of a button. All this Barlow outlines in his *Declaration of the Independence of Cyberspace*, penned while attending the annual World Economic Forum in Davos. The Declaration defined the basic tenets of cyberlibertarianism – the foundational free market, anti-regulation philosophy upon which Silicon Valley convened to build the World Wide Web as we know it today.

Missing from this historical narrative of the internet, however, is the role that sex workers have played in its development. The sex

worker has always been a major stakeholder in telecommunications. As Melissa Gira Grant notes in *Playing the Whore* (2014), 'Prostitution is a communications technology. It signals.' The term 'call girl' most explicitly exemplifies this, coined when city brothels were some of the first establishments to install telephone lines.

Substantial documentation places sexual labour as the driver of mass communications technology. In *The Erotic Engine* (2010), journalist Patchen Barss links the distribution of sexual material to the development of communications technology, including photography, home video and cable TV. 'Pornographers', Barss contends, 'were the technological pioneers who figured out how to make money from a new medium before the mainstream saw any profit potential.' Money made in the erotic market of 1980s proto-internet bulletin board systems (BBSs) literally paid for the material infrastructure that paved the way to the Web, as consumer demand for pornography and video games fuelled the push for better computer graphics, faster processing speeds and greater data bandwidths. All this made internet ubiquity a possibility. From there, a thread spinning at the rate of Moore's Law weaves adult content creators into the pattern of innovation towards the popular internet. They were also the first to invest in designing protocols for commercial search engines and livestream video, and to secure third-party payment processing.

Images throughout Sex-worker art collective Veil Machine staged a self-destructing online peepshow, called *E-Viction*, August 20, 2021

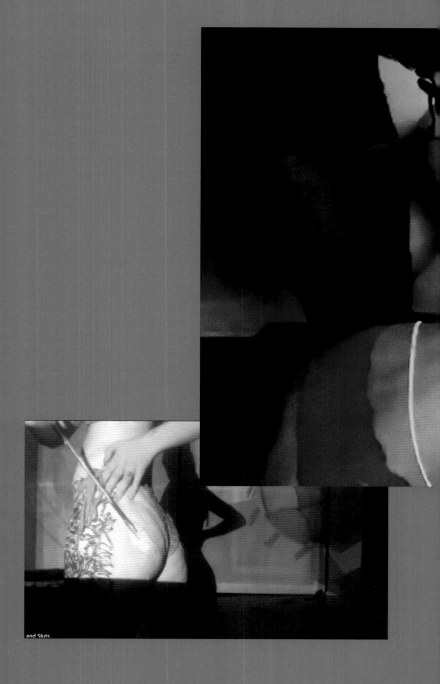

and Sluts

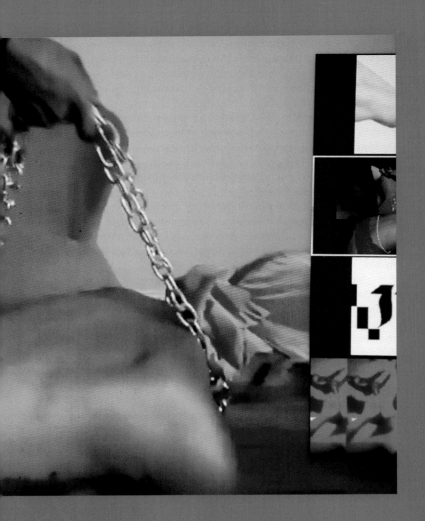

Early digital communities organised by and for sex workers were successful examples of the cyberlibertarianist future Barlow hoped for. They generated inclusive systems of self-governance that protected their members while challenging the very same state-sanctioned hostilities from which Barlow hoped to defend the internet. Whisper networks formed, creating digital catalogues of abusive clients and experiences of violence at the hands of law enforcement. Reliance on third-party management, aka 'pimps' and 'madams', declined as workers connected directly with clients through inde-pendently posted online advertisements. Identity tracking through digital fingerprints discouraged client-perpetrated violence against sex workers soliciting online. Whether through the ability to inde-pendently produce sexual content or to solicit online from the safety of home, digital mediation made sex work an attractive source of income for those who might never have thought of participating in sex trades before.

Most critically, an international, intersectional decriminalisation movement in response to the violence experienced by sex workers at the hands of clients, managers and the police coalesced online on a scale previously impossible. Sex workers and their allies organ-ised digital platforms that offered legal, medical and harm reduction resources. These visible alliances worked towards legitimising the trade. While the internet as we know it today was popularised by – and made accessible through – the sex industry, it simultaneously provided a venue in which those ostracised by the systemic and often state-sanctioned weaponisa-tion of sexual stigma could gather.

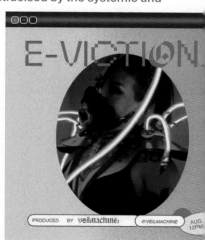

SETTLING THE FRONTIER

Today, there is little evidence of the ethics-based self-governance Barlow envisaged would arise from those pioneering the New Digital World. Instead we live in a cyber-netic dystopia riddled with algo-rithmic bias, viral misinformation and the erosion of privacy by way of data mining. What's more, none of this was actually instigated

or enforced by the government as Barlow predicted, but rather through a surveillance economy driven by private sector platforms. These, ironically, continue to thwart state intervention except when the government invests in and protects them, usually through public-private partnerships that provide user data to help develop surveillance technologies for law enforcement. How did this happen?

JARNING!!
fection(s)
found!!

anted Anti-Trafficking viruses
been detected in your system.
will be "saved." Actually, you
will be abolished.

[ok?]

Rather than pointing to the state, Barlow should have been looking at his peers. He missed the important fact that his utopia was occupied by techno-privileged early adopters, who seized on the opportunity to freely capitalise without oversight or accountability. Zeynep Tufekci documents this phenomenon in her 2016 essay 'As the Pirates Become CEOs: The Closing of the Open Internet' which traces the growth of 'walled gardens', or privately owned digital spaces acting as public commons. According to Tufekci, 'the open Internet that held so much generative power took a turn toward ad-enhanced platforms' such as Facebook or Google, which 'enabled, and forced the creation of massive, quasi-monopolistic platforms, while incentivising the platforms to use their massive troves of data with the power of computational inference to become better spy machines, geared toward ad delivery'. In short, this state of affairs has corrupted the evolution of the internet: it has gone from being a place of cyber-libertarian possibility to one of corporate tyranny, in which a handful of platforms are in a race to obtain the biggest user dataset possible.

In this deterministic dystopia, digital communities have become commodities to be siphoned off and sold, and their members are the ultimate product.

DIGITAL CHARACTER

'What social groups are classified, corralled, coerced, and capitalized upon so others are free to tinker, experiment, design, and engineer the future?' This is the driving question behind Ruha Benjamin's *Captivating Technology* (2019), in which she brings to light the

injustices caused by technologies built to 'classify and coerce certain populations'. Tech development, Benjamin argues, is distorted by what she calls a 'carceral imagination' in which technology 'actually aids and abets the process by which carcerality penetrates social life'. Amazon's camera-equipped Ring doorbell, for instance, now delivers its video footage warrant-free to over 1,800 police departments across the United States through Neighbors, its 'neighbourhood watch' app.

In this ad-based surveillance economy the entire experience of the internet is one of being taxonomised and prodded, pried into for information, and subjugated to the ideals of a hegemonic system. Benjamin exemplifies this through her description of the digital character, 'a digital profile assessed to make inferences regarding character in terms of credibility, reliability, industriousness, responsibility, morality, and relationship choices'. Benjamin traces how marketplace lenders follow the digital foot-steps of these characters – their social media activity, transaction histories, location data – to determine a person's creditworthiness. But assessed according to which standards? As Benjamin explains, these technoscientific designs are informed by hegemonic norms and standards historically defined within the context of white male supremacy, thus perpetuating deep, discriminatory disparities along race, gender and class lines.

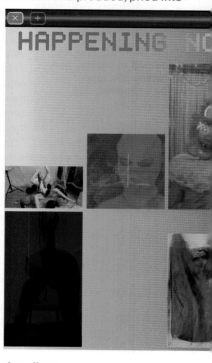

Benjamin is at variance with Barlow, who didn't understand the potential material impact of commodified networks. When he claimed cyberspace as 'a world that is both everywhere and nowhere, but it is not where bodies live', Barlow believed that physical coercion could not occur in the digital realm. However, the surveillance of our digital lives – whether for policing or for selling – directly impacts the ways that people can move through the world, both digitally and physically.

CANARY IN THE COALMINE

The elimination of sex work online is sold to the public as 'cleaning up' the internet for the safety of its users. It's hard to argue against the idea of making it a more hospitable place. But when you dissect the insidious reason why – which is to extract, collect and sell as much user data as possible for the benefit of a few corporate giants – it becomes imperative to probe into how sex work became the prototype for policing cyberspace.

A regular tactic has been to conflate consensual sex work with messages about sex trafficking in order to garner public support for the surveillance and censorship of online behaviour. This blanket censorship was codified into US law with the 2018 passage of the SESTA-FOSTA Acts, which amended the Communications Decency Act so that online service providers would be held criminally liable for any use of their platform that 'promotes or facilitates prostitution'. The argument was that this would help curb child sex trafficking, an assertion that has since been proved false. The laws created the internet's first US government-sanctioned censoring instrument, instigating websites to make definitions of obscenity even broader in order to protect themselves from SESTA-FOSTA's sweeping scope. This resulted in the banning of much lawful speech, from forum discussions about alternative sexual identities, through sexual health and education materials, to resources promoting sex worker safety.

Worse yet, through algorithmic content moderation software, the sex worker has become an object model on which surveillance technologies are trained. By proving that they can target and weed out society's chosen 'deplorables' with precision, walled-garden platforms advertise their ability to meticulously extract and classify user data, a desirable feature for companies that want to push users towards their products. These technologies parallel – and inform – technologies for predictive policing, protest surveillance and migration control.

The evolution from the cyberlibertarianist ideology of the internet to a corporate one has been especially devastating to sex workers. In *Erased*, a community-led report highlighting the impacts of platform policing, Hacking//Hustling found that reduced access to online spaces for sex workers has led to a 73 percent increase in financial instability, as well as a 34 percent increase in experiences of violence at the hands of clients. Further, financial tech platforms such as PayPal or Venmo algorithmically assess user profiles and online activities to

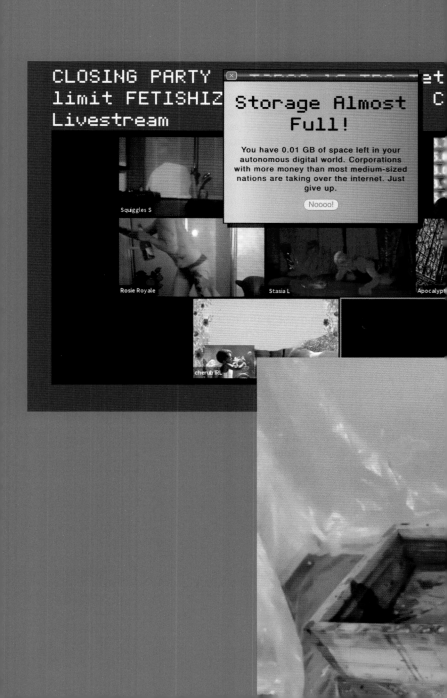

CLOSING PART...
    fetishizati...
CENSORSHIP
...tion of a   am
...H US

CRITICAL ERROR: YOU'VE FALLEN IN LOVE WITH A WH0RE

You've reached the end. Did you find what you were looking for? Did you get what your mouth watered for, what your body twitched for? Well that's it. "You don't have to go home but you can't stay here." How many times have we heard that....

But What We Have is Real!

Talking:

Zoom Group Chat

From E-VICTION BOUNCER to Everyone:
$15: Pie me
$22: Naked for 30 minutes
$122: Naked for the rest of the show

$12: Pop balloon / re-fiill w/ syrup (maple/chocolate/strawberry)
$15: Pop balloon / re-fill w/ paint
$18: Pop balloon / re-fill w/ custard
$21: Pop balloon / re-fill w/ spaghetti O's & sauce
$24: Pop balloon / re-fill w/ cake batter
$27: Pop balloon / re-fill w/ mayonnaise
$30: Pop balloon / re-fill w/ gunge/slime
$33: Pop balloon / re-fill w/ slop (5+ items your choice)
$50: Pop MASSIVE balloon w/ entire gallon in it (your choice of mess)

To: Everyone ▾   ⋯

Type message here...

identify and ban customers who have ever engaged in sex trades, even if they do not use those platforms for income.

In a sick twist, Big Tech has figured out how to pimp the entire world, both using and discarding the sex worker in the process. This parallels Ruha Benjamin's overview of carceral technologies that end up applied to civil society. What is built on the premise of 'protecting the public' only first affects the marginalised before bleeding into the general population, reproducing social hierarchies and reinforcing biases along the way. Key issues such as data surveillance and censorship that sex workers have been calling out have finally begun to have traction. Documentaries such as *The Social Dilemma* (2020), and *The Great Hack* (2019) are finally mainstreaming conversations about the devastating damage to society caused by surveillance economy platforms. But how much harm could have been avoided if we didn't have to wait for a bunch of white tech bros to confirm what sex workers had been telling us years before?

DIGITAL VICE RAIDS

It is helpful to think of this platform sanitation as an extension of 'urban renewal projects', more commonly known as gentrification. In *The Gentrification of the Mind* (2012), Sara Schulman describes how, on the brink of bankruptcy in the 1970s, New York City began to design urban renewal policies with the objective of attracting affluence back into the city after the exodus of its tax base to the suburbs. 'White flight', which was at least partially encouraged by a manufactured '"fear" of or alienation from urban culture, from multiculturalism, gender nonconformity, and individuated behavior', had driven working class whites out of the city in search of suburban lifestyles. In hopes of re-attracting those who had fled, the city provided tax breaks for the development of luxury condominiums, and quelled remaining fears of urban culture through the 'quashing of public life'.

Gentrification is often sold to the public as making the streets 'safe' but the question is, for whom? Schulman duly notes that neighbourhood 'safety' comes at the expense of its original inhabitants, for whom the neighbourhood is now dangerous. Grant connects sex work's movement into the private sphere to this quashing of public life, which occurred through crackdowns on deviant sexual behaviour in semi-public spaces in order to make room for real estate and private interest development. 'Through zoning and through fear-

fuelled bias, sexually oriented businesses have been isolated from "legitimate" businesses', which Grant notes were simply 'neighbors' among 'sites of labor – theaters, food carts, camera shops, shoe shine stands, hustlers'.

So the policing of behaviour becomes financially motivated, and there's no one better to guarantee a homogenised morality than the vice squad, a division of law enforcement specifically designed to discipline moral offences. Vice patrols were created in the late 1800s to infiltrate spaces suspected of encouraging immoral behaviour, which were often established by those who had drifted towards urban centres in search of upward mobility. These spaces – legal brothels, immigrant-operated businesses, dance halls that allowed for interracial mingling – grew out of a collective experience of disenfranchisement.

Immoral behaviour was criminalised under the false pretence of saving (white) women from the presumed horrors of coerced sexual labour. In her 2017 essay 'The Virtues of Unvirtuous Spaces', Alexandra Levy writes how the legislation based on this surveillance, codified finally as the Mann Act (known then as the White-Slave Traffic Act), was 'aimed at combatting "trafficking in women," but… was actually used to punish against all kinds of heterodox sexual practices, including miscegenation, polygamy, adultery, and promiscuity'. Besides the horrifically racist enforcement of this law on consenting interracial couples, the 'slavery' from which it promised to save (white) women left no room for sex work as a choice, whether it be the more lucrative alternative to underpaid female industrial labour, the consenting means by which someone got passage to the US, or a matter of basic survival.

It should be no surprise then that part of FOSTA is actually an extension of the Mann Act, expanding it to create a new federal crime 'prohibiting the owning, operating or managing of an interactive computer service, such as a website, with the intent to promote or facilitate… prostitution'. From this angle we can see how the Mann Act, which prosecutes based on the movement of bodies through space,

skews to designate interactive computer services as vehicles capable of transport in order to legally justify the surveillance of digital space and the policing of digital selves.

If we concede that order in cyberspace can be obtained by physical coercion, why don't we call the shuttering of sex-work-friendly spaces online what it is? These are vice raids. This makes digital gentrification only the most recent iteration of a long tradition of criminalising behaviour in order to pave the way for private interests.

RADIO IMAGINATION

At the time of writing the world has spent over a year in various stages of Covid-19-related isolation. Yet all the lockdowns in the world could not wipe sex work from the face of the planet. Sex workers on the privileged side of the digital divide moved their work online, joined by thousands of newcomers who entered the digital sex industry after losing their jobs. Less than a month into the total lockdown of New York City, *The New York Times* reported a major increase in digital sex work, noting that trade-facilitating platforms experienced spikes in sign-ups. OnlyFans, for instance, disclosed 3.7 million new accounts created between March 1 and April 10, 2020.

The pandemic mainstreamed what sex workers have known all along: when push comes to shove, people will dismantle the status quo in order to survive. This moment in time makes space for a 'radio imagination', a term coined by Octavia E Butler and applied by Ruha Benjamin to define a 'methodological touchstone for ethical engagement with technoscience, where the zeal for making new things is tempered by an ability to listen to the sounds and stories of people and things already made'.

PRIVACY ERROR

Warning! Your privacy has be breached. Your connection is secure.Just kidding!!! Privacy this day and age?? Hahahaha

As if!

So what of these 'things already made' by sex work, things like, literally, the internet, fostered into being due to the potent combination of an instinct to survive, the body's creative force and the height of human imagination, also known as fantasy? What

can be discovered if we explore the metaverse that the sex worker calls home, where reductive binaries are relics of an antiquated religion, and the pursuit of expressive connectivity drives evolution? Would all that be so bad?

A better question: is the cost of keeping us from doing so in order to preserve ideals of extractive capitalism worth it?

Society's supposed deplorables have been remarkably good at taking care of one another. They're necessarily resilient and adaptive, shapeshifting to suit their surroundings. This command of the liminal has become an especially useful skill for sex workers campaigning against the gentrification of the internet. There has been no better recent example of this than *E-Viction*, a digital riot organised by sex worker art collective Veil Machine in response to the violence experienced by sex workers targeted by technology developed to identify and eliminate them. In a 12-hour-long act of civil disobedience, *E-Viction* defied digital vice laws by platforming sex worker ads, performances and resources on an interactive website built by the collective. This reclamation of space presented a momentary glimpse into the pre-gentrified internet before 'self-destructing' at midnight, reproducing the loss experienced by the razing of sex-work-friendly spaces across the internet.

This is technoscientific 'radio imagination' fuelled by the sex-worker vision. It is resourceful, ephemeral, confrontational and empathetic. Veil Machine member Niko Flux notes that the use of language historically associated with the tangible landscape has been especially helpful for this mission, because it stresses the material impact of digital action. Thinking in terms of eviction, for instance, enabled the collective to imagine what an act of civil disobedience could look like in the time of Covid, in which all interaction has been moved to the screen. Designing this project with definitions of eviction and gentrification also pushed the collective to approach the project as spatial planners. Making an immersive world, Flux says, involves creating a sense of wonder or discovery. 'It's like directing movement through mystery,' she remarks, 'the things that only happen when there are shadows or alleyways.'

Civic activist Jane Jacobs identified how the sterilisation of urban neighbourhoods in the name of 'renewal' or 'slum removal' often had the opposite effect, instead leading to neighbourhood decline. Healthy neighbourhoods require eyes on the street, Jacobs says, 'eyes belonging to those we might call the natural proprietors', to keep both residents and strangers safe. This can only be facilitated by creating

paths of discovery – short blocks and alleyways – which diversify foot traffic. 'In city districts that become successful or magnetic, streets are virtually never made to disappear,' Jacobs writes. 'Where it is possible, they multiply.'

By building a back alley into the restricted space of the internet, Veil Machine showed us what an internet with 'eyes on the street' can look like. Flux notes that this requires asking:

> How do you create something that's exclusive enough to protect people, but not accidentally exclude people from being able to participate? How can we guarantee funding from ethical sources, and make sure the resources are flowing in the right direction, so that we are supporting our community?

Imagine a world in which these are the types of questions intrinsic to the development of telecommunications, rather than the ones that have led to the commodification of our digital selves. Imagine an internet built by those who innovated out of a need for collective safety, rather than by those driven to conquer a global economy. Imagine a cybernetic future founded by those who are forced to imagine, by those for whom the creative functions of both mind and body have never been severable. Where discrete boundaries can never be drawn, and we are excited by a movement through mystery. Which we may never fully understand but do not have to, because we can entrust our 'red light neighbours' with the task of watching over corners that daylight does not cover, signalling outwards to a network that adapts to disruption.

NETWORK ERROR

You've reached the end. Did you find what you were looking for? Did you get what your mouth watered for, what your body twitched for?

We really wish we could stay and chat, engage in some pillowtalk, cuddle, and fall asleep in your arms. Unfortunately, we have to go; we're on the run. Do you mind locking up after you leave? You don't have to go home but you can't stay here.

They can try to keep on killing us, to put their hands over our mouths, but they can never keep us away. We'll be back.

In the mean time, remember us by the absence we've left behind. This is the hardest part. The loneliest moments are the ones that accompany a detaching: space that was first empty, then filled, then emptied again.

Amplify sex worker voices. **Contact** your representatives about FOSTA/SESTA and EARN IT. If you work in tech, **push** for change from the inside.

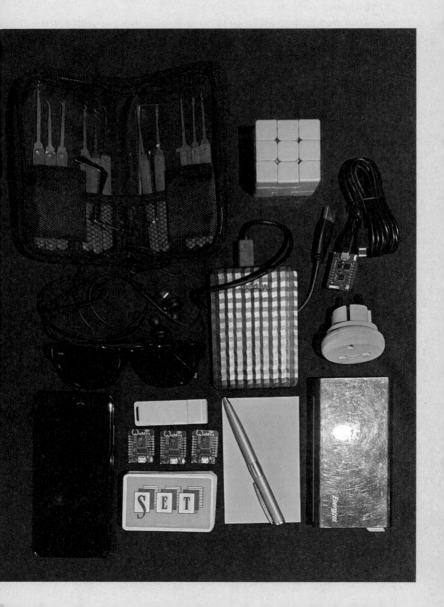

Joe Lloyd   Hello, Jake? Where are you?

Jake Davis   Hi I'm in a forest. Just finding a tree that is covered.

JL   First things first, could you tell me about your time as part of the Anonymous hacking collective?

JD   That was around 2010, 2011. I was 16 or 17. And, spoiler alert, I was arrested for it at around 18. I got involved in chat rooms that were marketed as Anonymous. I liked the idea of a faceless collective hive mind. Still now I think it's a very intriguing use of the internet. It appealed to me more than the hacking itself. The internet is used for these banal things and corporate marketing, and these guys are doing something really interesting. At that point I'd spent so much of my childhood sitting in front of a screen that I became very close to this kind of internet culture, this hive mind.

JL   So what happened then?

JD   I got into activism, defending the freedom of the web, empowering different people around the world to use the web. At the time I thought we were going to overthrow dictators. I ended up writing Anonymous messaging, most notably against the racist, homophobic cult, the Westboro Baptist Church. I had a big feud with them and hacked all their websites. It was a bit of a mistake on my end, not ethically, but from a security point of view. I spoke to them using my real voice and that, and various other things, led to my eventual demise from that realm.

JL   You were also part of another hacking group, LulzSec?

JD   Our goal was essentially to mock security. We thought at the time, in a very naive, reckless way, that we would improve global security by exposing flaws in everything, wherever possible. The bigger the target the better. We hacked the CIA, the Senate, FBI affiliates and large corporations. We wanted to say 'Look, we're not even trying very hard and we've managed to potentially gain access to all of your lies.'

JL   How did that go down?

JD   I ended up in court but they weren't quite sure how to prosecute because there was no financial gain or intent to destroy. For example, we hacked *The Sun* in response to the phone hacking scandal where they would hack the voicemails of celebrities and their relatives, even deceased relatives, to get information. We thought this was really

Previous page   Portrait of his phone by Jake Davis

egregious hacking. We had access to *The Sun*'s infrastructure but decided not to leak any of their files. We just posted ridiculous fake news articles from their website.

JL   How did you first learn to hack?
JD   I like to ask the same question when I'm at hacker conferences. Most hackers have the same answer: we start by tinkering. For me, I started playing video games and wanted to make mods for the game *Halo*. I wanted to know how to get Linux on the Xbox and to get maps edited in the game. That transplanted into computers because a games console is essentially a computer. From there, it's just participation and presence. I became involved in hacker communities from a very young age and so I would open my laptop and just see it all the time, I'd see people talking about it and would absorb it.

JL   Recently, with phenomena like Zoombombing, the media perception of hacking seems to be broadly negative.
JD   If you look at the term 'hacker' in 2020s media, they're usually referring to ransomware, where people try to extract large sums of money from companies in return for files. These people are described as hackers, but I would never think of them as hackers. And wouldn't even a decade ago. We'd just consider them fraudsters or criminals.

JL   How does computer hacking compare to phone hacking?
JD   Both require a broad understanding of how to reverse-engineer programmes. People who go after phones reverse-engineer apps. It's like certain branches of maths: there are only a few dozen people that really get something. The main difference between the two though is in understanding how information moves, from phones to base transceiver stations and masts, and how this can be intercepted with hardware.

JL   How easy is it to hack a phone?
JD   Phones are weak, from a hardware and a human perspective. There's a reason that when people go into highly sensitive meetings everyone turns off their phone, takes the batteries out and puts them in a microwave. Phones are moving 24/7 wiretap devices. You're vulnerable not only to hacking, but to something that could be worse: the complete upheaval of your personal information to any old random government entity that turns on your camera or your mic. That problem exists with all devices, but the phone is in our face all the time. People

sit on the toilet with their phone. It's weird that we've normalised having this thing in our pockets all day that anyone can get information out of.

JL Do you think hacking has done more good or bad?
JD That's a very tough question. Overall it's a force for good. Even if we only hear about the ransomware, and nation states attacking nation states. There's a weaponisation to it that can never be good but that would be true of any emergent technology. And the latest technology has always been exploited for oppression and war. So hacking is going through that.

JL So what will become of hacking in the future?
JD A lot of the stuff we're talking about now will seem completely primitive and absurd in a quantum age, when our computer power becomes so exponential that the issues we have now will seem ridiculous. The only real way to fix our security problems is to tear up the entire internet and start again.

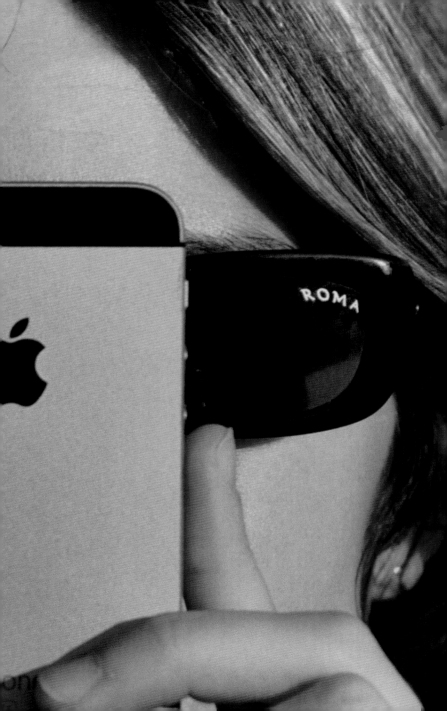

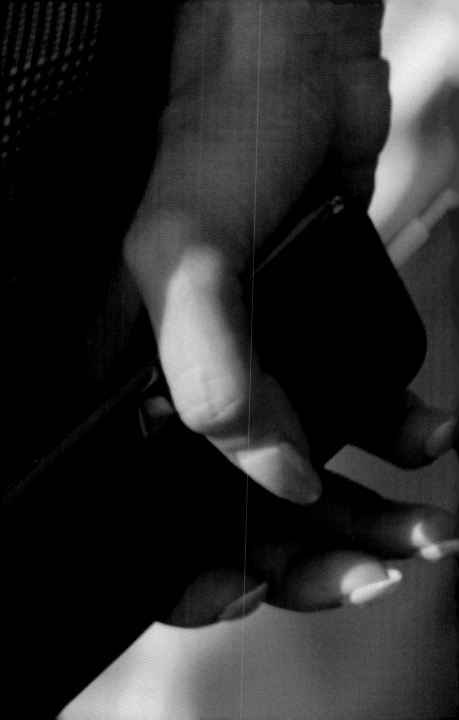

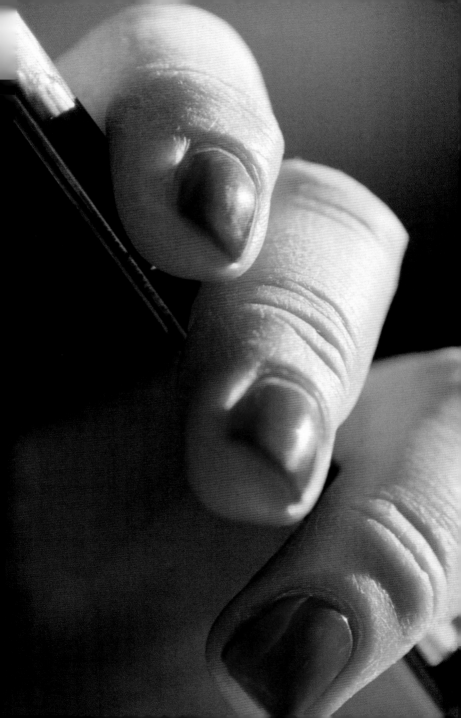

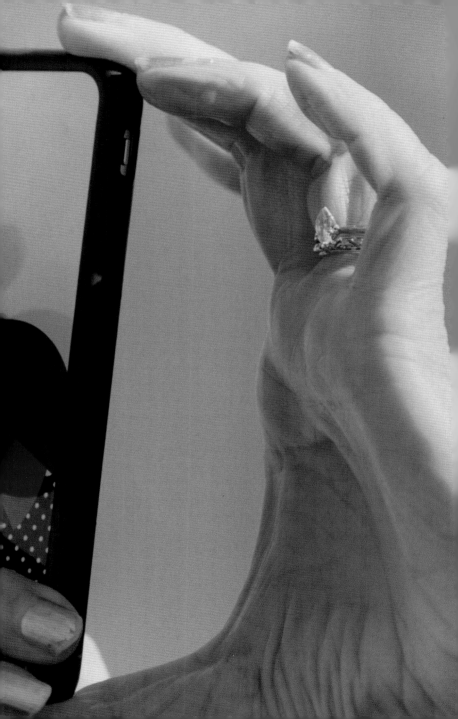

A BODY ALIVE WITH SIGNALS

PAUL ELLIMAN ON THE PAR

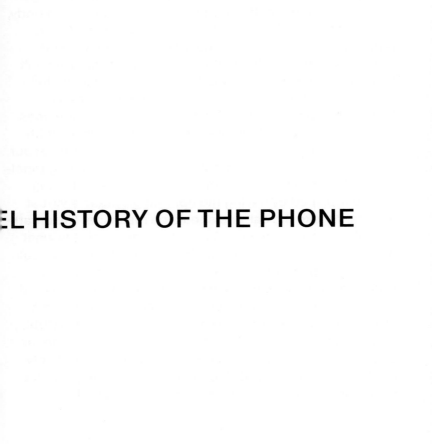

EL HISTORY OF THE PHONE

During the Covid pandemic we were invested in the search to secure viral protection that would work as well as the virus protection software installed on our phones. While our phones and computers now felt relatively safe, the virus had triggered our greatest fear: it made us feel human. I began to wonder if some of the unique senses of the human body, fast losing ground to the mass production of machined parts, apps and extensions, could perhaps be recalled.

Clearly there are things the phone can do that we can't. From the Greek *tēle*, 'far away', and *phōnē,* 'voice', its full name explains as much; the telephone lets us speak to people in places where we are not. But the phone does more than just this. It replaces the things we can do with its own version: the touch of our hands, the structure of our memory, our sense of orientation, the ever-extending topologies of social life. Finally, the use of a phone for talking can be replaced by having the operating system's virtual assistant make the call and speak the message. The unfathomable distance between Siri and a human voice is what the name 'telephone' now implies to me. Whatever we call this form of phenomenological uncanny, it situates the phone in a media-ecological network of devices that hold many of the sensory functions of our body at remote distances from ourselves. In his final book, *Chaosmos* (1992), Felix Guattari described the threat to life on our planet as a consequence of the damage we have inflicted not only on the environment, but also on the social fabric, affected by the ways that we communicate with one another.

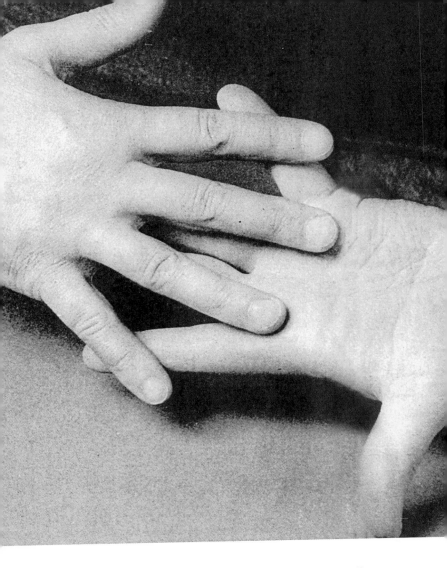

VOICE   Even you and I share in the invention of the long-distance propagation of a human voice. Shouts and calls, cries and loud hailing are almost as old as the hills. The Scandinavian *kulning*, for example, is a yodelled herding call sent hundreds of metres across mountain pastures, often sung by female shepherds and cattle herders.

Far away, the grazing animals respond with their own lowing calls. As they start to move, their tuned bells signal the sound of the herd moving down the mountain towards home.

But how did the human voice become an object not of the human body? Human speech has been released like the 'wandering voice' in Wordsworth's poem *To the Cuckoo* (1807), heard in the trees and the distant hills as if embodied by them rather than the creature that it once belonged to.

The re-embodied voice is the product of a collective nineteenth-century focus on mechanical devices that could transmit vocal messages. Twenty years before Alexander Graham Bell's 1876 telephone and Thomas Edison's 1878 wax cylinder phonograph, the Parisian typesetter Édouard-Léon Scott de Martinville received a patent for his invention of the phonautograph. The device used a horn to collect sound, while a single brush bristle connected to a rotating cylinder covered with lampblack registered the sequence of vocal sound waves. With a fragile sooty sonograph, Scott de Martinville had the first recording of a human voice, but his machine was unable to play it back in sound.

Scott de Martinville's phonautograph was a brilliant attempt to engineer key features of the way our ears receive and transcribe sound waves. It is the ears rather than the mouth that provide the main focus for development of the telephonic voice. Both voice and ears are a remarkable example of adaptive signal and sensory system co-evolution. As Bill Bryson points out in *The Body: A Guide for Occupants* (2019), hearing is an undervalued miracle:

> *Imagine being given three tiny bones, some wisps of muscle and ligament, a delicate membrane and some nerve cells, and from them trying to fashion a device that can capture with more or less perfect fidelity the complete panoply of auditory experience – intimate whispers, the lushness of symphonies…*

A key influence on attempts to re-embody the voice is Hermann von Helmholtz's *On the Sensations of Tone* (1863). The first chapters offer a kind of field guide to the human ear. Annotated drawings of all its parts resemble a wiring manual for the construction of a small transistor radio, to which this work was to be something of a precursor. Von Helmholtz also describes manual experiments to extend the vocal tones of a human voice by singing into the strings of a piano. He was looking for ways to replicate mechanical processes at work in the human ear and voice. He knew that every fibre of the ear's auditory nerves is connected with electric parts. And the

Images throughout   A Body Alive with Signals by Paul Elliman, 1986–ongoing

combined efforts of his research and knowledge seemed to all but invent the transmissive voice of the telephone.

Following the advanced ideas of Scott de Martinville, von Helmholtz and others, Alexander Graham Bell and Clarence J Blake constructed their own phonautograph in 1874. It received attention partly because it used an actual human middle ear, a tympanum removed from a corpse, to collect the sound waves. Bell also described the mapping of the parts of the body to the mechanical device, comparing the mouthpiece to the external ear, the air chamber to the middle-ear cavity. Bell was a teacher of vocal physiology and the son of an elocutionist. His mother lost her hearing when he was in his teens, and Bell learned a manual finger language, spending many evenings tapping the family conversations into her hand. It was her impairment that led him to study acoustics as part of a continuation of his father's work on speech and elocution.

Inventors of the telephonic voice had to figure out its relationship to the human ear in order to resolve the problem of getting it to arrive somewhere intact. In 1854 Charles Bourseul developed an electromagnetic microphone, but his telephone receiver was unable to convert electric current back into clear human voice sounds. The voice arrived in a hail of shattered pieces, fragments of electrical static. In 1856, while making progress with an early telephone, Antonio Meucci was also developing a treatment for rheumatism using electric shocks. He heard the scream of a patient through the copper wire he was testing to conduct sound. Meucci recognised that the 'tongue' of copper was vibrating in the way that a gold-leaf electroscope detects static electricity. Though unintended, his first successful vocal transmission was a cry of pain.

The first call between Alexander Graham Bell and his assistant Thomas Watson was not the famous one. On June 2, 1875, when a transmitter spring jammed, Watson plucked it more forcibly, accidentally making a permanent contact with the spring. The circuit remained unbroken, with the magnetised vibration doing exactly as Bell had speculated: transmitting a faint echo of the sound of the spring that had generated it. Attesting to Bell's ability to perceive the 'transcendent importance of that faint sound thus electrically transmitted', as Watson wrote in his autobiography, the speaking telephone was born at that moment. 'Bell knew perfectly well that the mechanism that could transmit all the complex vibrations of one sound could do the same for any sound, even that of speech.' Bell's patent was issued the following year, March 7, 1876.

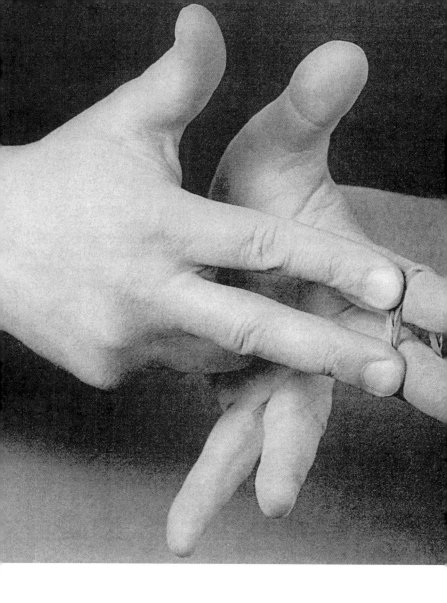

HANDS Embryologists perceive the hand as a kind of antenna fitted to the beam of the arms and equipped with high-sensory organs that we call fingers.

Embryology also gives a clue how the hand evolved. Emerging from the body as buds, these become paddles, then arms and hands before extending into a brachiating limb, facilitating continuous interaction with the surrounding environment.

Raymond Tallis, philosopher and consultant surgeon, describes the hand as a medium for psychical, physical and emotive social communication. Tallis was inspired by a 1998 doctoral thesis by Paulette van Vliet. It focused on patients who had sustained a stroke affecting the arm, after reaching for a glass, either empty or half full of water. The study convinced Tallis that our body's movements are not driven by conscious agency: too many variables, too much precision required. The action was done by customised motor programmes in the arm and hand that can be triggered as required.

Film-maker Robert Bresson was obsessed with this relationship between agency and mechanism. He spoke of his preference for actors to follow the 'automatisms that make up so much of a body's life'. As Bresson would say, 'When your hand is on your knee, you didn't put it there.' In many of his films, ordinary hands play the subtle protagonists of everyday life. It brings to mind eighteenth-century novels of circulation, their tales told from the perspective of an object of exchange, passed hand-to-hand between brief owners. In an example from Thomas Bridges' 1770 novel *The Adventures of a Bank-Note*:

> ... by the Yorkshire clothier, I was paid to a wool-stapler; he paid me to a Nottingham weaver; the weaver changed me with the landlord at the Bull in Bishopsgate-street; the landlord paid me to the one-eyed Norwich warehouse-keeper; from him I went to a gingerbread-baker for gingerbread sent by the waggon into the country. By Timothy Treaclebread the gingerbread-baker I was paid to Mrs Coppernose, a rich brazier's widow, for rent: all this was performed in less than three hours.

To keep our hands handling something, anything, seems part of an ancient rite of haptic connection. The first possession of a soft toy or a small blanket is said to mediate the mother's separation. The social life of the hand involves it also as a form of speech. Hand gestures precede and then accompany speaking in children. The talking hand includes its many signifying uses both friendly and hostile, intimate and formal. Tallis points out that from a doctor's perspective hands are explicitly informative, 'laden with signs of disease', and that 'touching the body, one seems to lay a hand on lived time'.

Historians describe surges of change in the social structure of European cities between 1550 and 1800. Centred in the rapidly expanding network of coffee houses and salons, spoken discourse began to merge with the signifying status of personal objects. Psychoanalyst Darian Leader, in his study of hands, suggests that people's fingers were kept busy with their gloves, timepieces and snuffboxes in ways that carried the same air of self-sufficiency as a phone might today. Soon the cigarette became a primary social object. Launching his campaign against tobacco in 1664, King James I asked, 'And is it not a great vanitie, that a man cannot heartily welcome his friend now, but straight they must bee in hand with Tobacco?'

The cigarette is now rapidly disappearing from social life, yet, as Leader points out, 'something has miraculously taken its place: ... mobile phones now colonise exactly the same social and bodily spaces'.

The naming of the digits is traced to the Vikings in the time of the Danish rule of England. They also introduced generous laws about reparation for the loss of fingers, with high compensation rates for the thumb and ring finger, which may have had mystical significance. Latin variations on the Viking names are used by anatomists today: *digitus auricularis*, the little finger, relating to the ear or hearing, is used to extract wax from the outer ear; *digitus demonstratorius*, the index finger, for indicating; The ring finger, *digitus anularis*, known in King Alfred's Anglo-Saxon as *goldfinger*, was also *digitus medicinalis*: doctors wore a gold ring on that finger. 'Pinkie' is thought to derive from *pink*, a Scottish term for a little boat, or *lytlafinger* in Anglo-Saxon. And the middle finger, *digitus impudicus*, is the unchaste one; it slips gently into the intimate pockets of a body.

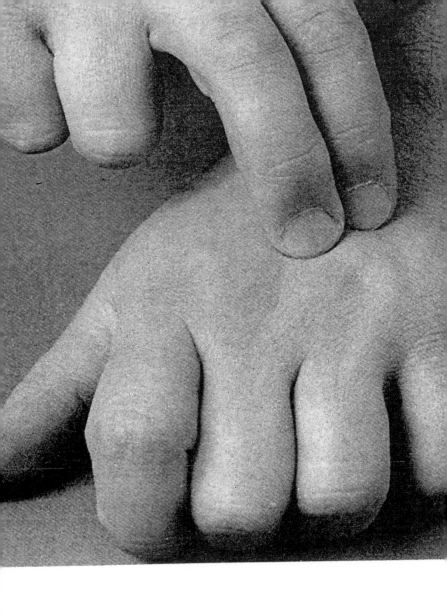

MEMORY Memory often feels fragmentary. Fittingly, scholars of ancient memory practices usually work with physical fragments.

In *The Art of Memory* (1966), historian Frances Yates refers to the remnant of a parchment known as the Dialexeis, from around 400 BCE. Only a few brief lines remain, reminding us: 'A great and beautiful invention is memory, always useful both for learning and for life.'

We tend to think of memory in relation to language; it is part of the cognitive process of knowing and perceiving things. But memory occurs across the entire body in non-verbal ways we are less conscious of until, as with our machines, something goes wrong. A stroke can result in loss of voice and memory, and so reveal some of the mysteries of human memory.

In *Pieces of Light* (2013), psychologist Charles Fernyhough explores the effect of certain memory anomalies. He meets Jill Price, one of only 10 people known to have hyperthymestic syndrome. Locked into near total recall, Price remembers explicit details from every day of her life since age 14. October 3, 1987? 'That was a Saturday. Hung out at the apartment all weekend, wearing a sling – hurt my elbow.' Fernyhough also talks with neuropsychologist Chris Moulin, one of a small group of scientists studying persistent *déjà vécu* – a déjà vu-like illusion comprising a continuous sense of having previously lived through everything that you experience. The condition was first discussed in France in the 1890s in an attempt to distinguish between several kinds of paramnesia. A 34-year-old man named Louis, recovering from cerebral malaria, described the sensation of 'recognising' almost every experience as 'like living in two parallel years'.

In our phones and computers, memory refers to ways data is stored and accessed. In logistical terms it refers to metal-oxide-semiconductor (MOS) memory. Data is stored within MOS memory cells on a silicon integrated circuit chip. Unlike the long-suffering Price, people have no internal data log to scroll through. While we perceive memory as backward-focused, it functions in present time. Its evolutionary role is keyed to learning from everyday experiences to anticipate future events and situations.

Computers remember very differently. The equivalent to a brain cell is a tiny switching device called a transistor. State-of-the-art microprocessors contain over 30 billion transistors, all packed onto an integrated circuit smaller than a postage stamp. But here any comparison between computer and brain ends. Transistors are wired in relatively simple, serial chains, each connected to two or three others. A human brain contains billions of tiny neuron

cells with clusters of connections. Glial cells support each neuron by providing energy that helps them grow and maintain contact with thousands of neighbours. Our body is thus a model of socially collaborative energy. Our devices less so, making us more susceptible to algorithmically generated information aimed at social coercion and division.

Not long ago, computer memory was woven by hand. In the late eighteenth century Joseph Marie Jacquard used cards with punched holes as a mechanism for operating a weaving loom. The card was an important precursor to the development of computer programming. Charles Babbage, known as the father of the computer, knew of Jacquard's machines and planned to use cards to store programmes in his Analytical Engine. By the 1950s IBM was leading a data processing industry using punched-card technology, until the early 1970s.

For the 1969 Apollo Space Programme, a new form of software known as 'core rope memory' was manually woven into a high-density storage system. Producing it was entrusted mostly to women from the textile industry. Facing each other at long desks, they hand-strung tiny doughnuts of ferrite material on wires – each wire passed back and forth through a matrix of eyelet holes about the diameter of a pencil lead. The eyelets were a magnetic core bead. Passing a wire through the core created a 'one'; by-passing the core, a 'zero'.

Core memories disappeared with the introduction of semiconductor memory. Entire memory systems can be replaced. We like to feel we're moving on, convinced by the newest system upgrade.

Travelling in Peru in 2007, I was offered a set of pre-Columbian Quechua bracelets, each a collection of mnemonic objects strung together: small votive charms, stones and shells, seeds, bone, glass and wooden beads, a coin, a tooth, a small brass bell, a tiny hand amulet, a small metal spoon, explained to me as memory chains. Each was a sort of shepherd's calendar holding a record of the village over a lunar year. They would be read in a trance by the shaman or head of the village, handling the objects, tasting or smelling the story of the village, telling it in hummed songs, breathing sounds, animal cries and bird calls, with some parts spoken in Quechua, the main language family of the Inca Empire.

I asked the shopkeeper how he came to have them. He explained that a man he knew in the village had brought them in. The tribe had converted to Jehovah's Witness. The bracelets no longer worked; they were obsolete.

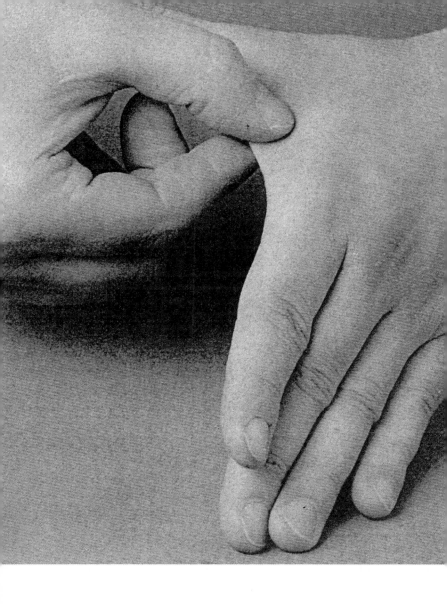

NAVIGATION   Our sensory interactions with the world rely on most of the same bodily functions as prehistoric humans. But today we cover more distance and travel faster.

How we orient ourselves was relatively unchanged until around 2000, when we started to outsource the cognitive part of finding our way to GPS-enabled devices and software. The unofficial consensus among scientists is that for the first time in human evolution, we have abandoned the spatial skills that sustained us over many thousands of years.

Perhaps to counteract this loss, a closer interest in how animals negotiate the world has followed. Animal behaviourists describe how, until recently, this area of research was largely ignored because what it claimed seemed too incredible to believe. The reality of what insects, birds, whales and so many others are capable of was so mysterious that even famously wise heads attributed it to acts of magic. Aristotle claimed that redstarts transformed into robins in winter, and garden warblers became blackcaps.

Seventeenth-century English scientist Charles Morton proposed that storks flew to the moon 'in one great flock' for their winter break. Attributing migratory habits to magic and space travel is better than a tired anthropomorphism that denies the possibility of things we don't fully understand. All we really know is that natural selection has led to a range of sensory systems unheard of until studies of the behaviour of bees and pigeons brought a very different response.

On long annual journeys to Mexico, monarch butterflies use a range of navigational tools. Changing their orientation to the sun at different stages of the day and latitude, they are aware of magnetic field activity, crosswinds and visual landmarks by day. They calibrate to the Milky Way at night. The impressive navigational systems used by monarchs are shared by many creatures, including us. The first aviators calculated their position in the sky by using a previously determined position and then incorporating estimations of speed, direction and course over elapsed time. Bees keep track of distances through shared information between the vestibular system and their wing beats. Saharan desert ants measure their footsteps.

There are also sensory instincts that we have forgotten or neglected. Freud described the loss of chemical senses in humans as the consequence of our pursuit of hygiene. Research into the human vestibular system often begins from studies of how we sense gravity, then comparing our sense of orientation with other creatures whose own seems far better developed. In birds, signal activity between the inner ear, a protein in the retina called cryptochrome, and magnetite crystals in the beak is believed to activate cells sensitive

to the geomagnetic field. The same components are found in the human body. Magnetite in the hippocampi supports our use of spatial memory and the ability to navigate our movements.

Studies suggest that speakers of languages that avoid simplifying terms such as right and left, north and south, may have stronger spatial memory and better navigation skills. Their language reflects the rhythm of the surrounding environment. To an outsider, the Arctic landscape might seem featureless. Yet the Inuit names of locations, many of which are centuries old, are part of a cognitively sharpened wayfinding inclination.

Science writer Michael Bond describes how, when the English explorer George Francis Lyon passed through parts of the Canadian Arctic in 1822, he noted that 'every streamlet, lake, bay, point, or island has a name, and even certain piles of stones'. But even so, a typical example from his naval chart of 1823 shows that newly renamed Sir James Lancaster Sound is the landing inlet locally named Tullurrutiup Imanga, or 'water surrounding land resembling facial tattoos on the chin'.

The pioneers of early long-distance aviation were forced to rely on raw instincts. At least, French aviation pioneer Antoine de Saint-Exupéry, who devised his own navigational and landing tools, gives that impression in his writing; he constantly refers to weather, tides and constellations – and how they affect the body and connect it to the world. According to Saint-Exupéry, 'when wild geese migrate in their season, a strange tide rises in the territories over which they sweep'. As if magnetised by the flock, farmyard birds feel the ancestral urge to follow, a taste of the ocean already sensed in their awakening vestibular systems.

As Saint-Exupéry reminds us, technology doesn't solve the problems of the body; it makes us more aware of them. And while it's always a mistake to assume any sense of what it's like to be another creature, he found in the air a kinship with the long-distance migratory journeys of a bird or a butterfly, a body perceptually embedded in its flight.

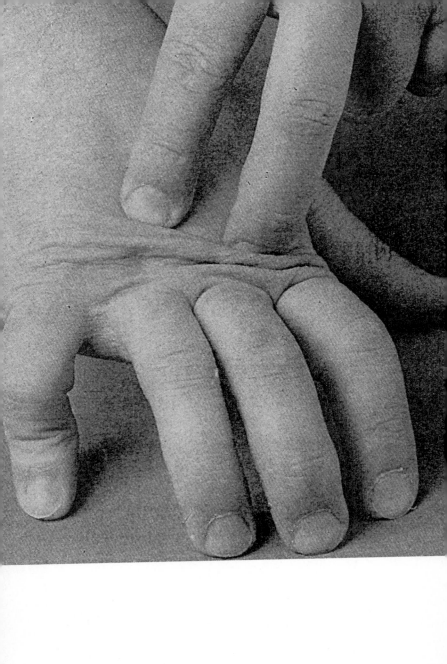

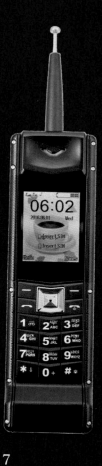

7

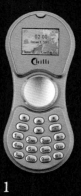

1

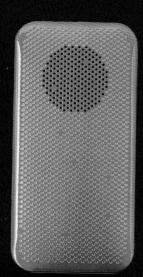

2

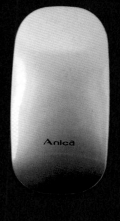

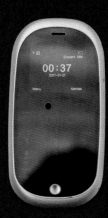

6

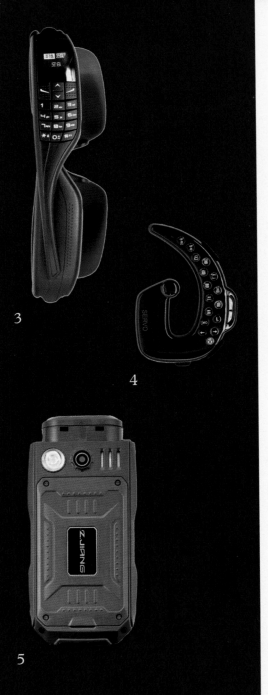

AN ARCHAEOLOGY OF SHANZHAI PHONES BY DISNOVATION

Shanzhai is a term used in China to describe objects that are counterfeit or just plain crappy. Meaning 'mountain village', the name signals its association with mountainous Shenzhen, the city where – thanks to loose copyright enforcement and tax regulations – the 'Made in China' industrial revolution began.

Here, in the early 2000s, an incredible number of small plants specialising in making and assembling toys, clothes and electronics emerged. Over time, these manufacturers learned to disassemble, recreate and sell these products.

Hybrids
1   Fidget spinner phone
2   Sound system phone, aimed at older people in China, who often gather in public squares to play mahjong and sing and dance to music outdoors.
3   Sunglasses phone
4   Headset phone
5   Shaver phone
6   Mouse phone
7   Power bank phone, sold primarily in Accra, the capital city of Ghana, where frequent power outages can make charging a phone difficult.

SHANZHAIJI

Shanzhaiji (*shanzhai* phones) were made possible by the emergence of MediaTek phone kits.

After Western companies, such as Intel, began standardising computer parts in order to maintain profits, small factories began to follow Intel's and other companies' guidelines to produce the required components. In the 1990s factories began to sell these computers directly to customers and resellers abroad, leading to a surge of no-brand 'white box' personal computers. That's when Taiwanese electronics manufacturer MediaTek applied the same strategy to cell phones.

Selling cheap, bare-bones phone kits directly to smaller factories meant anyone could collaborate with a cousin specialising in plastic toy moulds to create a new dolphin phone.

Hybrids
1 Buddha phone, a knock-off of the *Wellwishing Zen* phone, designed as a digital accompaniment to Buddhist prayer and related religious activities (such as the burning of incense).
2 Wooden phone
3 Zippo lighter phone
4 iPhone case phone
5 Pen fan phone
6 Cigarette lighter car phone
7 Card phone

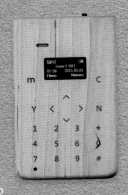

2

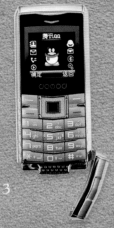

3

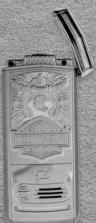

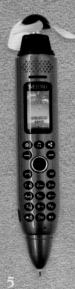

5

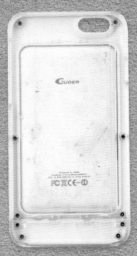

4

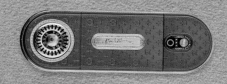

1

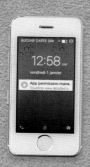

2

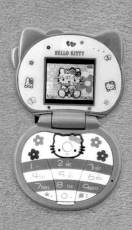

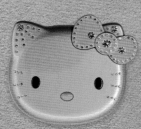

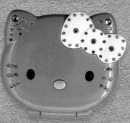

7

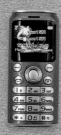

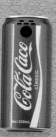

6

DECLINE OF SHANZHAI

For the city of Shenzhen, stories of the *shanzhai* factories are part of a foundational mythology, even though most plants were forced to close down many years ago by rising land costs or reform campaigns. By the 2010s, many of the original factories were undeclared or just plain illegal. Most factory owners were migrants from other parts of China who relied extensively on informal networks from their villages of origin. Rising costs and competition with larger firms made the release of products harder, leading to less frequent seasonal assembly and the gradual departure of factory workers.

Copycats
1 Louis Vuitton phone
2 Mini iPhone
3 Marlboro phone
4 Porsche key ring phone
5 Apple phone
6 Cola-Caco phone
7 Hello Kitty phone

SHENZHEN NOW

Today, very few original accounts of life in these factories exist. Working conditions in these plants were harsh. But now Shenzhen is home to some of the world's biggest technology companies, including Huawei, Xiaomi, DJI and BYD, and is internationally recognised for its highly flexible and rapid manufacturing ecosystem. Sceptics argue the sharing culture of *shanzhai* held China back from this path to modernisation. Others maintain the culture of copying became the very catalyst for innovation.

Tactical phones

1 Prisoner phone, originally marketed as the world's smallest mobile phone; it soon gained notoriety because, 99 percent made of plastic, it was barely detectable by security checks at airports and prisons. Later models came with a voice changer to modify the voice of the caller.

2 Mini flip phone
3 Ghana phone
4 Mini Nokia phone
5 Walkie-talkie phone
6 Power bank phone
7 Grenade phone

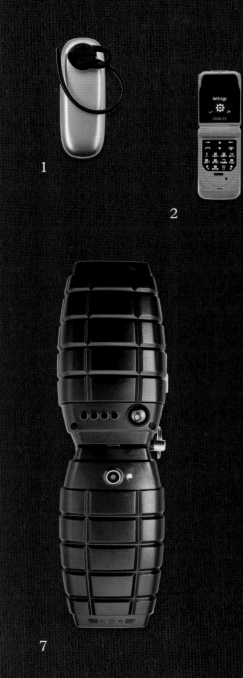

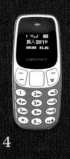

4

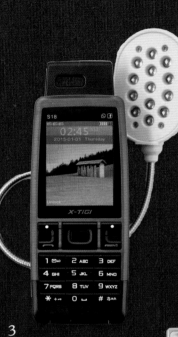

3

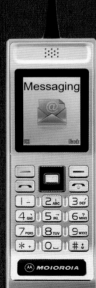

6

5

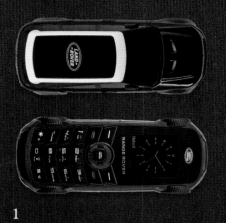

1

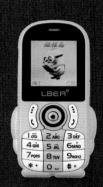

2

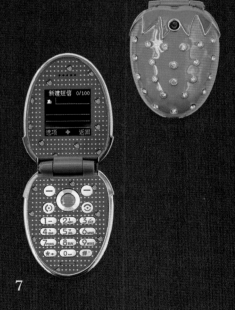

7

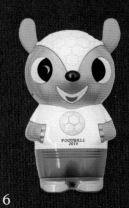

6

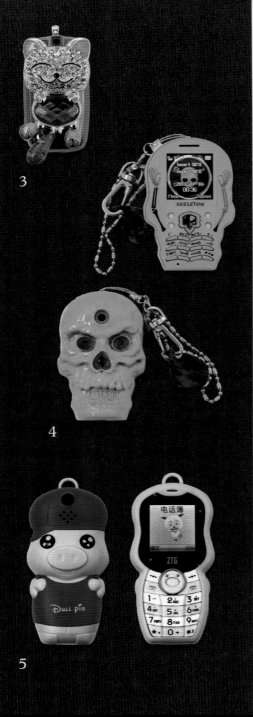

COLLECTING SHANZHAI

The act of displaying Chinese artifacts in the West bears a striking resemblance to that of the orientalist cabinet of the nineteenth century. The notion of counterfeiting informs most discussions about the Chinese electronics industry. But it's worth remembering the story of French Jesuit priest Father d'Entrecolles, who arrived in China as a missionary in 1698. In 1712, after visiting Jingdezhen, the capital of famed Chinese porcelain, he wrote a letter to a fellow Frenchman revealing secret details, which he had witnessed at first hand, of how the precious pottery was cast. His divulgence would, a few decades later, give birth to the European porcelain industry. It is ironic that Victorian England and Napoleonic France's most refined goods originated from such a blatant case of industrial espionage – and counterfeiting – on a continental scale.

Toys
1 Land Rover phone
2 Minion phone
3 Jewelled Kitty phone
4 Skeleton phone
5 Dull Pig phone
6 Football mascot phone
7 Strawberry phone

If I am to write anything of quality, my phone has to be in another room, with the Wi-Fi disabled. This is a minor cheat, of course. The only real way to write something meaningful is to turn the handset off and leave it in a separate building.

There's always a sharp sting of anxiety before depressing the power button. I don't know why. I mean there's a lot of anxiety everywhere. There may be more anxiety than depression. It depends who you ask. When they were born. What their moon sign is. How much phone battery they have left.

YOUR NETWORK IS OUT OF RANGE

YOU HAVE 532,652 UNREAD EMAILS

Technology is inextricable from power, the kind that shapes society and politics. Why do we use the same word to describe the phenomenon that obsessed Michel Foucault and the energy which charges our phones?

Technology is meant to save us from many non-technological discomforts. Instead, technology invents new pathologies that wouldn't exist otherwise.

YOU DO NOT HAVE ACCESS RIGHTS

IS THIS REALLY YOUR FACE?

The media theorist Marshall McLuhan famously wrote that 'all technologies are extensions of our physical and nervous systems'. This was in the 1960s, an era of television, radio, magazines and adverts: a time of popular media shaping societies, economies and subcultures.

McLuhan wasn't exactly a humanist, but this thesis feels decidedly anthropocentric. He was saying that everything we make – our tools, our media – emanates from our bodies and our minds. We are cause, technologies are effect.

Somewhere in the past decade, when it comes to our mobile phones, such relations have drastically and dramatically reversed. *We* are now an extension of our phone. We are *its* prosthesis. The phone is cause, and we are effect.

This is a new power relationship. Let's call it The Great Reversal. History is littered with these switches, moments where the magnetic poles of meaning reverse. In the fifteenth century, Gutenberg ushered in the age of the printing press. This began a process of decentralising knowledge, which led to profound political consequences. A century later,

YOUR UPGRADE
IS READY

Copernicus shifted the centre of the universe from Earth to the Sun, which was considered an act of blasphemy by the Church. And four centuries after that, Freud designated the unconscious as a place where a truer self resides, making human appearance less important than what lies underneath. The Great Reversal is in this lineage of existential, philosophical and epistemological ruptures.

The effects of The Great Reversal are so seismic we have barely begun to fully apprehend them. We are too busy being changed, and commenting on each other's changes. At least the ones we can see and feel. Truthfully, it's all the changes we can't sense that are changing us the most. These are the changes we should be most concerned with, most vigilant about, but –

SEE YOUR HISTORY

YOUR ACCOUNT HAS BEEN BLOCKED

There are people who will always think the pandemic was a hoax. There are people who won't vaccinate their children. There are people who have burned down 5G masts to stop the spread of the virus.

The breakdown of consensus-based reality is one of the most dangerous threats facing current shared human experience. This tendency accelerated the moment humans became extensions of their phones.

People no longer passively wait for the truth to be presented to them. People actively choose the version of truth that suits them best. If one person hallucinates something, they're considered mentally unstable. If millions share the same hallucination at the same time: that's now reality.

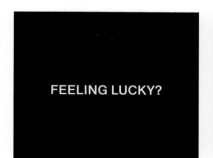

January 6, 2021. The State Capitol, Washington, DC. Outraged that Donald Trump was about to officially lose the Presidential election, thousands of Americans waged an assault on the building, with intentions to kidnap politicians, and maybe even kill them.

The background to this insurrection was a volcanic spew of libidinal force, formed, formatted and conjured in chatrooms and message forums and on social media. Here, they fermented their worldview. They then decided to LARP (live action role play) at the State Capitol. The day after, most went back to their normal lives as school teachers, pool cleaners and bank clerks.

Remember Second Life, the 3D virtual world released in 2003? Its name implied that the world around us is first life, and the one in your phone is second. What happened on January 6 was the inversion of that.

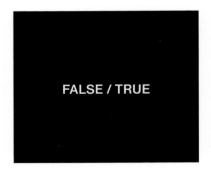

In the film *Minority Report* (2002), 'precogs' detect a crime before it has even happened. Their brains are attuned to waves sent out from a future event to the present moment.

Today, algorithmic suggestions – of what to read next, what to watch next, what to buy next – command power from knowing what you want before you know you want it. This brings up age-old questions about free will: did you decide to buy that limited edition distressed vegan leather clutch, or did your phone decide for you?

IF YOU LIKED THAT
YOU'LL LOVE THIS

NOTIFICATION

The phone hacks your free will. It lures you with its infamous dopamine hits, and has made you clinically dependent. Your memories are now stored in a top-security Microsoft server farm at the bottom of the ocean. You have outsourced parts of yourself and, in return, your phone takes over many of your neurological functions.

It thinks for you. It thinks you into being. It suggests people you should know, people you should desire, and the places where you should meet for consensual, guilt-free sex. This used to feel like striking coincidence. Now, it's more like predestination.

In the 1960s, going 'off-grid' meant leaving the city and embarking on a nomadic existence or settling in a desert or forest. Today, the equivalent emphatic rejection would be to smash your phone with a rock. *Be phoneless*. Adrift in the information wilds. You would tell the world, in person, that you reclaimed your sense of agency. You would become a voluntary refugee from the deluge. 'I am no longer an extractable extension to technology. I am neither message nor media. I am "delinked".'

YOU HAVEN'T POSTED IN A WHILE

ARE YOU AN INDEPENDENT THINKER?

In his most recent novel, *The Silence* (2020), Don DeLillo writes, 'What happens to people who live inside their phones?' For context, it is 2022 and suddenly, one night, every piece of technology – televisions, planes and yes, phones – stops working. It reminds me of how, early in the pandemic, I paraphrased Slavoj Žižek paraphrasing Fredric Jameson, by telling my friends that 'it is easier to imagine the end of the world than the end of the internet'. Imagine our lockdowns without our phones. Isn't that what the apocalypse would be for our generation? Joshua Cohen, reviewing *The Silence* in *The New York Times*, agrees:

the increased chance of the world ending not with a bang, or even a whimper, but in silence… the silence that follows the blackout of our external brains, those silicon-celled devices to which we've transferred our timekeeping and cultural artifacts, our medical and legal records, our genetic sequences, our nudes, our novels, our pasts. This is the eschaton through lack of access.

It is worth noting here that DeLillo is 84 years old, and has been using the same typewriter since 1975. He is a technological dissident who manages to understand most acutely what damage technological totality has done to our souls.

**YOUR SOFTWARE
HAS EXPIRED**

Speaking of damage, a new phone doesn't become yours until it has been dropped and the sleek, perfectly smooth screen cracks. Every shatter is a unique form, a signature of molecules and matter reorganised into new order. As Jean-Paul Sartre wrote in *Being and Nothingness* (1943), 'My body is everywhere... the body always extends across the tool which it utilises.' The shattered screen reminds its user that this seemingly science-fictional thing, with its obelisk-like objecthood, is actually a mortal assemblage of elements, just like the human body. I like to watch people swipe their shattered screens, as if these were fetishistic scars on their own skin.

Here it is. The Great Reversal. You are the consequences of: the app you forgot to delete; an unreliable connection making you vulnerable to strangers; a battery that only charges to 69 percent, bloated by obsessive overcharging; a rear-facing camera that never focuses on the intended object. You became obsolete soon after you arrived in the world; OMGLOLIMHOTFWBRB; can you hear me?; you're stuttering; you're... stutter... ing; y 0 u ' r e s t u t t e r i

LOW BATTERY
10% REMAINING

YOU HAVE
NO POWER LEFT

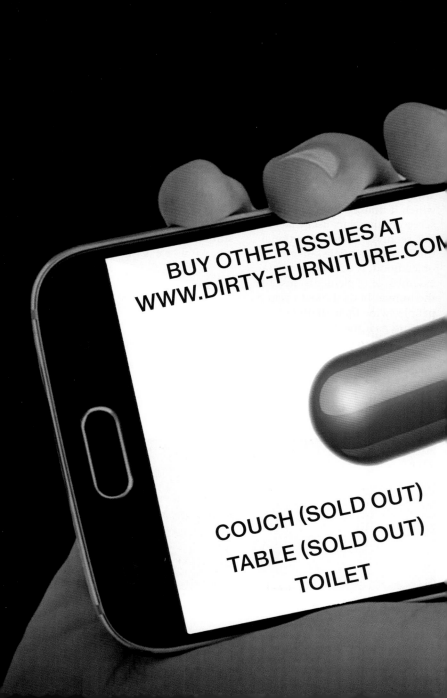

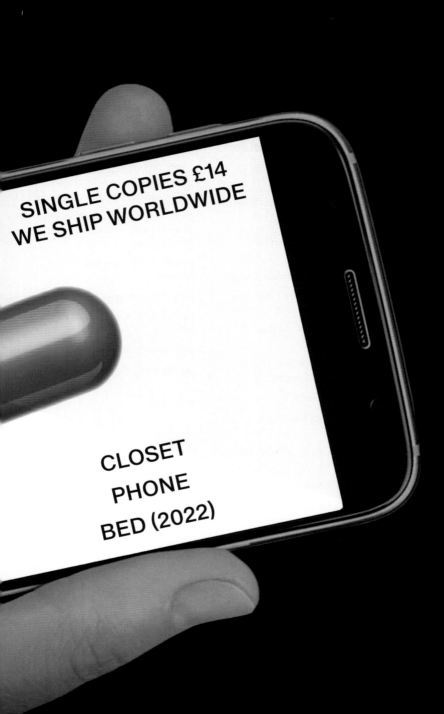

IMAGE CREDITS

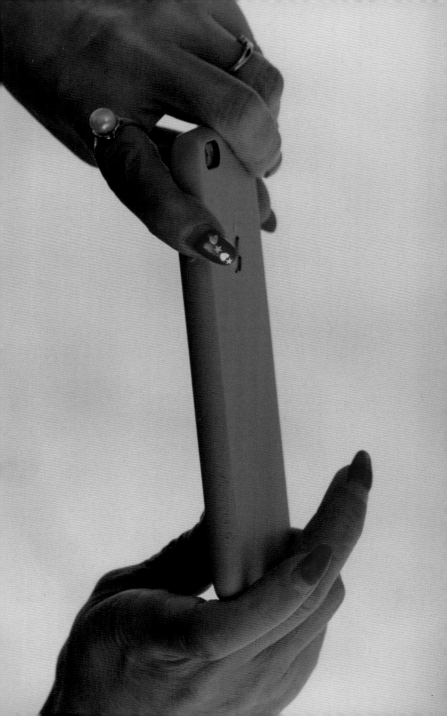

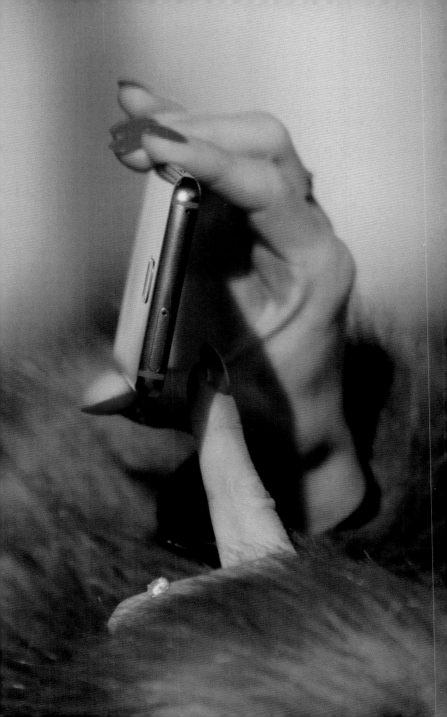

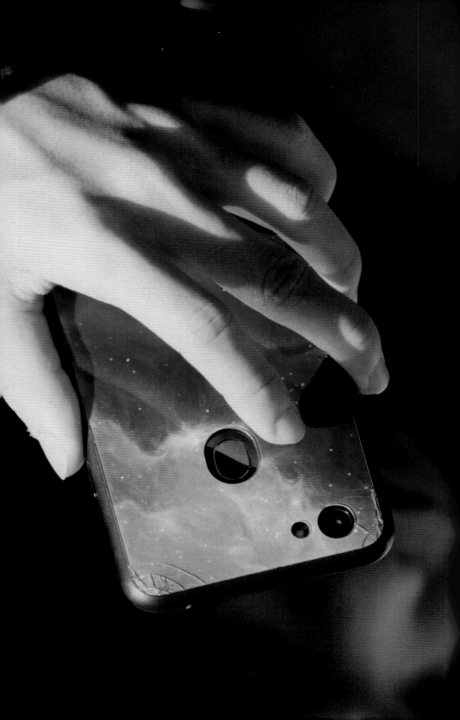

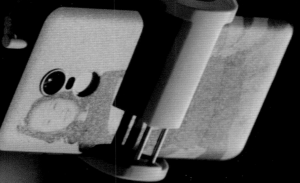